# ASCENT®
CENTER FOR TECHNICAL KNOWLEDGE

# Autodesk® Revit® 2024
# Fundamentals for MEP
# Part 2

*Learning Guide*

*Imperial Units - 1st Edition*

# ASCENT - Center for Technical Knowledge®
## Autodesk® Revit® 2024
## Fundamentals for MEP - Part 2
Imperial Units - 1st Edition

Prepared and produced by:

ASCENT Center for Technical Knowledge
630 Peter Jefferson Parkway, Suite 175
Charlottesville, VA 22911

866-527-2368
www.ASCENTed.com

Lead Contributor: Cherisse Biddulph

ASCENT - Center for Technical Knowledge (a division of Rand Worldwide Inc.) is a leading developer of professional learning materials and knowledge products for engineering software applications. ASCENT specializes in designing targeted content that facilitates application-based learning with hands-on software experience. For over 25 years, ASCENT has helped users become more productive through tailored custom learning solutions.

We welcome any comments you may have regarding this guide, or any of our products. To contact us please email: feedback@ASCENTed.com.

# Contents

## Construction Documentation

## Chapter 15: Adding Tags and Schedules — 15-1

## Chapter 16: Creating Details — 16-1

© 2023, ASCENT - Center for Technical Knowledge®

## Appendix A: Additional Tools for Design Development      A-1

## Appendix B: Additional Tools for Construction Documents      B-1

# Preface

To take full advantage of Building Information Modeling, the *Autodesk® Revit® 2024: Fundamentals for MEP* guide (Part 1 and Part 2) has been designed to teach the concepts and principles of creating 3D parametric models of MEP systems from engineering design through construction documentation.

This guide is intended to introduce you to the user interface and the basic HVAC, electrical, and piping/plumbing components that make Autodesk Revit a powerful and flexible engineering modeling tool. The guide will also familiarize users with the tools required to create, document, and print the parametric model. The examples and practices are designed to take users through the basics of a full MEP project from linking in an architectural model to construction documents.

## Topics Covered in Chapters 1 to 12 (Part 1)

- Introduction to the Autodesk Revit software, including navigating the Revit interface.

- Starting an MEP project based on a linked architectural model and creating levels and grids as datum elements for the model.

- Understanding the project browser and working with views.

- Understanding Revit families and components.

- Working with the basic sketching and modifying tools.

- Copying and monitoring elements and coordinating linked models.

- Creating spaces so that you can analyze heating and cooling loads.

- Connecting and testing basic systems.

- Creating pipe systems with plumbing fixtures and pipes.

- Creating duct systems with air terminals, mechanical equipment, and ducts.

- Creating advanced HVAC and plumbing systems with automatic duct and piping layouts.

- Creating electrical circuits with electrical equipment, devices, and light fixtures and adding cable trays and conduits.

## Topics Covered in Chapters 13 to 16 (Part 2)

- Setting up sheets, and placing and modifying views on sheets.

- Working with dimensions, text, annotations, and legends.

- Adding tags and working with schedules.

- Setting up detail views and adding detail components.

### Prerequisites

- Access to the 2024.0 version of the software, to ensure compatibility with this guide. Future software updates that are released by Autodesk may include changes that are not reflected in this guide. The practices and files included with this guide might not be compatible with prior versions (e.g., 2023).

- This guide introduces the fundamental skills you need to learn the Autodesk Revit MEP software. It is highly recommended that users have experience and knowledge in MEP engineering and its terminology.

- It is recommended that users have a standard three-button mouse to successfully complete the practices in this guide.

## Note on Learning Guide Content

ASCENT's learning guides are intended to teach the technical aspects of using the software and do not focus on professional design principles and standards. The exercises aim to demonstrate the capabilities and flexibility of the software, rather than following specific design codes or standards, which can vary between regions.

## Note on Software Setup

This guide assumes a standard installation of the software using the default preferences during installation. This includes the Revit templates and Revit Content (Families) that can be found on the Autodesk website at https://knowledge.autodesk.com/ by searching *How to download Revit Content*. Lectures and practices use the standard software templates and default options.

## Lead Contributor: Cherisse Biddulph

Cherisse is an Autodesk Certified Professional for Revit as well as an Autodesk Certified Instructor. She brings over 19 years of industry, teaching, and technical support experience to her role as a Learning Content Developer with ASCENT. With a passion for design and architecture, she has worked in the industry assisting firms with their Building Information Modeling (BIM) management and software implementation needs as they modernize to a BIM design environment. Although her main devotion is the Revit design product, she is also proficient in AutoCAD, Autodesk BIM 360, and Autodesk Navisworks. Today, Cherisse continues to expand her knowledge in the ever-evolving AEC industry and the software used to support it.

Cherisse Biddulph has been the Lead Contributor for *Autodesk Revit: Fundamentals for MEP* since 2020.

# In This Guide

The following highlights the key features of this guide.

| Feature | Description |
|---|---|
| **Practice Files** | The Practice Files page includes a link to the practice files and instructions on how to download and install them. The practice files are required to complete the practices in this guide. |
| **Chapters** | A chapter consists of the following: Learning Objectives, Instructional Content, Practices, Chapter Review Questions, and Command Summary. |
| | • **Learning Objectives** define the skills you can acquire by learning the content provided in the chapter. |
| | • **Instructional Content**, which begins right after Learning Objectives, refers to the descriptive and procedural information related to various topics. Each main topic introduces a product feature, discusses various aspects of that feature, and provides step-by-step procedures on how to use that feature. Where relevant, examples, figures, helpful hints, and notes are provided. |
| | • **Practice** for a topic follows the instructional content. Practices enable you to use the software to perform a hands-on review of a topic. It is required that you download the practice files (using the link found on the Practice Files page) prior to starting the first practice. |
| | • **Chapter Review Questions**, located close to the end of a chapter, enable you to test your knowledge of the key concepts discussed in the chapter. |
| | • **Command Summary** concludes a chapter. It contains a list of the software commands that are used throughout the chapter and provides information on where the command can be found in the software. |
| **Appendices** | Appendices provide additional information to the main course content. It could be in the form of instructional content, practices, tables, projects, or skills assessment. |

# Practice Files

To download the practice files for this guide, use the following steps:

1. Type the URL *exactly as shown below* into the address bar of your Internet browser to access the Course File Download page.

   *Note: If you are using the ebook, you do not have to type the URL. Instead, you can access the page simply by clicking the URL below.*

   **https://www.ascented.com/getfile/id/pristolepisPF**

2. On the Course File Download page, click the **DOWNLOAD NOW** button, as shown below, to download the .ZIP file that contains the practice files.

3. Once the download is complete, unzip the file and extract its contents.

   **The recommended practice files folder location is:**
   *C:\Revit 2024 Fundamentals for MEP Practice Files*

   *Note: It is recommended that you do not change the location of the practice files folder. Doing so may cause errors when completing the practices.*

   | | |
   |---|---|
   | **Stay Informed!**<br>To receive information about upcoming events, promotional offers, and complimentary webcasts, visit:<br>www.ASCENTed.com/updates |  |

# Construction Documentation

The third section of this guide continues to teach the Autodesk® Revit® tools, focusing on tools that help you to create accurate construction documents for a design.

This section includes the following chapters:

- Chapter 13: Creating Construction Documents
- Chapter 14: Working with Annotations
- Chapter 15: Adding Tags and Schedules
- Chapter 16: Creating Details

# Creating Construction Documents

The accurate creation of construction documents in Revit® ensures that the design is correctly communicated to downstream users. Construction documents are created primarily in special views call sheets. Knowing how to select title blocks, assign title block information, place views, and print the sheets are essential steps in the construction documentation process.

## Learning Objectives

- Add sheets with title blocks and views of a project.
- Enter the title block information for individual sheets and for an entire project.
- Place and organize views on sheets.
- Print sheets using the default Print dialog box.

# 13.1 Setting Up Sheets

While you are modeling a project, the foundations of the working drawings are already in progress. Any view (such as a floor plan, section, callout, or schedule) can be placed on a sheet, as shown in Figure 13–1.

**Figure 13–1**

- Company templates can be created with standard sheets using the company (or project) title block and related views already placed on the sheet.

- The sheet size is based on the selected title block family.

- Sheets are listed in the *Sheets* area in the Project Browser.

- Most information on sheets is included in the views. You can add general notes and other non-model elements directly to the sheet, though it is better to add them using drafting views or legends, as these can be placed on multiple sheets.

## How To: Set Up Sheets

1. In the Project Browser, right-click on the *Sheets* area header and select **New Sheet...**, or in the *View* tab>Sheet Composition panel, click (Sheet).

   - Alternatively, in the Project Browser, right-click on **Sheets (all)** and select **New Sheet...**.

2.   In the New Sheet dialog box, select a title block from the list, as shown in Figure 13–2.

   *Note: Click **Load...** to load a sheet from the Revit Library or your company's custom sheet.*

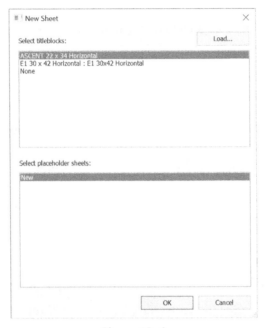

**Figure 13–2**

3.   Click **OK**. A new sheet is created using the selected title block.

4.   Fill out the information in the title block as needed.

5.   Add views to the sheet.

•   When you create sheets, the next sheet is incremented numerically.

•   Double-click on the sheet name to change the name and number in the Sheet Title dialog box.

•   When you change the *Sheet Name* and/or *Number* in the title block, it automatically changes the name and number of the sheet in the Project Browser.

•   The plot stamp on the side of the sheet automatically updates according to the current date and time. The format of the display uses the regional settings of your computer.

•   The Scale is automatically entered when a view is inserted onto a sheet. If a sheet has multiple views with different scales, the scale displays **As Indicated.**

# Sheet (Title Block) Properties

Each new sheet includes a title block. You can change the title block information in Properties, as shown on the left in Figure 13–3, or by selecting any blue label you want to edit (Sheet Name, Sheet Number, Drawn by, etc.), as shown on the right.

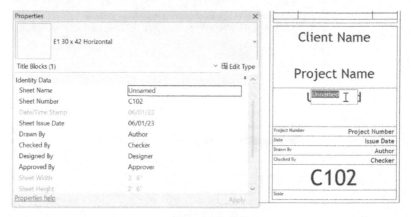

**Figure 13–3**

Properties that apply to all sheets can be entered in the Project Information dialog box (shown in Figure 13–4). In the *Manage* tab>Settings panel, click 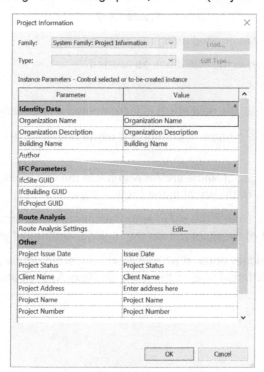 (Project Information).

**Figure 13–4**

# 13.2 Placing and Modifying Views on Sheets

The process of adding views to a sheet is simple. Drag and drop a view from the Project Browser onto the sheet. The new view on the sheet is displayed at the scale specified in the original view. The view title displays the name, number, and scale of the view. Once the view has been placed on a sheet, the icon next to the view name in the Project Browser is filled in.

## How To: Place Views on Sheets

1. Set up the view as you want it to display on the sheet, including the scale and visibility of elements.

2. Create or open the sheet where you want to place the view.

3. Select the view in the Project Browser, and drag and drop it onto the sheet.

   *Note: Alignment lines from existing views display to help you place additional views.*

4. The center of the view is attached to the cursor. Click to place it on the sheet.

- Views can only be placed on a sheet once. However, you can duplicate the view and place that copy on a sheet.

- Views on a sheet are associative. They automatically update to reflect changes to the project.

- Each view on a sheet is listed under the sheet name in the Project Browser, as shown in Figure 13-5.

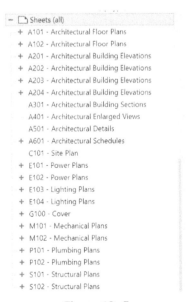

**Figure 13-5**

## How To: Add Multiple Views and Schedules to a Sheet

1.  Open a sheet that you want to place views on.

    *   In the *View* tab>Sheet Composition panel, click 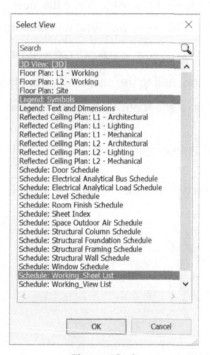 (Place View). Alternatively, in the Project Browser, right-click on the sheet name and select **Add View...**.

2.  In the Select View dialog box (shown in Figure 13–6), you can use the search at the top of the dialog box to narrow down the views in the list, then use <Shift> or <Ctrl> to select multiple views you want to use and click **OK**.

    *Note: This method lists only those views which have not yet been placed on a sheet.*

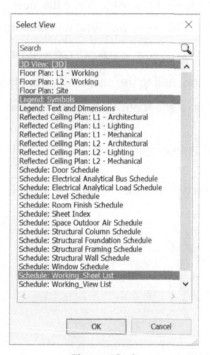

**Figure 13–6**

3. The views will be attached to your cursor, as shown in Figure 13–7. Click to place the views on the sheet.

**Figure 13–7**

- Alternatively, you can open a sheet that you want to place views on. From the Project Browser, use <Shift> or <Ctrl> to select multiple views, then drag them to the sheet.

- To remove a view from a sheet, select it and press <Delete>. Alternatively, in the Project Browser, expand the individual sheet information to show the views, right-click on the view name, and select **Remove From Sheet**.

# Open Sheet

To open sheets from the Project Browser, you can double-click on a sheet from the *Sheets (all)* section. As the project gets larger, you can easily open multiple views, schedules, legends, and 3D views directly from the drawing area or from the Project Browser.

- In an open view with nothing selected, right-click and select **Open Sheet**, as shown in Figure 13–8.

**Figure 13–8**

- Select multiple views (e.g., plan views, 3D views, schedules, and legends) that have the placed on sheet indicator next to them, as shown in Figure 13–9. Right-click and select **Open Sheet**. Click **OK** in the Open View dialog box to open all the sheets.

**Figure 13–9**

# 13.3 Swapping Views on a Sheet

You can reduce the time it takes to modify the views that are placed on a sheet by quickly swapping out a view with another view from the ribbon or Properties.

- You can swap a view on a sheet with a view that is already on another sheet.

- When swapping views, you can specify if you want to retain the view title's position from a viewport's Type Properties, as shown in Figure 13–10. When **Preserve Title Position** is checked, the view title will resize to the viewport when a different size view is swapped.

**Figure 13–10**

## How To: Swap a View on a Sheet

1. From the Project Browser>*Sheets* node, open the sheet view.
2. Select the view that is on the sheet.

3.  In the *Modify | Viewports* tab>Positioning & View panel, expand the views, as shown in Figure 13–11, and select one from the list. You can use the search bar to filter the list.

    • Views already on sheets will have suffixes at the end of their names with the sheet number.

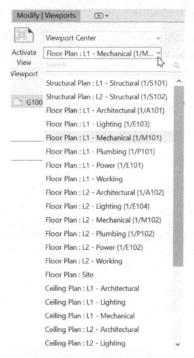

**Figure 13–11**

4.  If you select a view that is already on a sheet, the View Already Placed dialog box will display, as shown in Figure 13–12.

**Figure 13–12**

5. Select **OK** to swap the view.

- Alternatively, with the viewport selected, in Properties, in the *Identity Data* section, change the *View* on the sheet by expanding the parameter's drop-down list and selecting a different view, as shown in Figure 13-13. If you select a view that is already on another sheet, the View Already Placed dialog box will display.

Figure 13-13

## How To: Drag a View Aligned to Another Sheet

1. In the Project Browser, *Sheet* section, expand a sheet and select one or multiple views, right-click, and select **Move View Aligned to Sheet...**, as shown in Figure 13-14.

Figure 13-14

2.  In the Select Sheet dialog box, select a sheet and click **OK**, as shown in Figure 13–15. The view moves to the sheet, keeping its original alignment.

    * To quickly find a sheet from the list, use the search bar at the top of the dialog box.

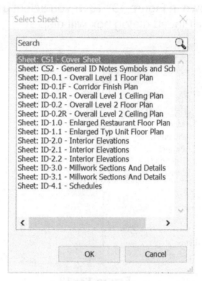

**Figure 13–15**

* Alternatively, under the *Sheet* section, expand a sheet and manually drag a view to another sheet. The view is moved and keeps its original alignment.

## Removing Views from a Sheets

There are three ways to remove a view from a sheet:

* In the Project Browser, select one or multiple views, right-click, and select **Remove From Sheet**, as shown in Figure 13–16.

**Figure 13–16**

- If multiple views are selected, click **OK** in the Remove From Sheet dialog box, as shown in Figure 13–17.

**Figure 13–17**

- In the Project Browser under the *Sheets* node, you can expand the sheet, select the views, right-click, and select **Remove From Sheet**, as shown in Figure 13–18. If multiple views are selected, click **OK** in the Remove From Sheet dialog box.

**Figure 13–18**

- You can remove a view directly from a sheet by selecting the view and pressing <Delete>.

# Duplicating Sheets

Duplicating a sheet will add a suffix of *Copy 1* after the sheet name, as shown in Figure 13–19. It will also automatically generate with the next available sheet title number, like G101 shown in Figure 13–19.

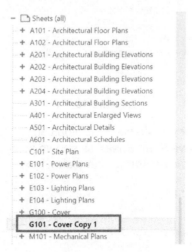

**Figure 13–19**

## How To: Duplicate Sheets

1.  In the Project Browser>*Sheets* node, right-click on a sheet and select **Duplicate Sheet**.
2.  Select one of the following options:
    *   **Duplicate Empty Sheet:** Creates a new sheet with the same titleblock and project information.
        *   No model or annotation elements on the sheet are duplicated.
    *   **Duplicate with Sheet Detailing:** Creates a new sheet with the same titleblock, project information, and any legends, keynotes, schedules, and annotations.
    *   **Duplicate with Views:** Before a sheet gets created, you are prompted to specify how you would like the views on the sheet to be duplicated, as shown in Figure 13–20.

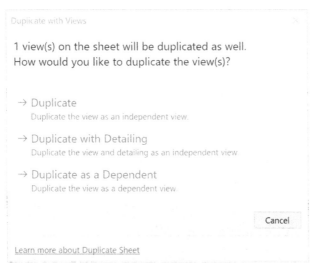

**Figure 13–20**

*Note:* To review duplicating view types, refer to *Working with Views.*

- In the Duplicate with Views dialog box, select **Duplicate**, **Duplicate with Detailing**, or **Duplicate as a Dependent**.
- If you are duplicating a sheet that has drafting views and want to duplicate the view with the model and annotation elements, you need to use the **Duplicate with Detailing** option.

# 13.4 Modifying Views and View Titles

After you have the desired views on a sheet, you can modify their locations and titles. You can use some of the modify tools, like **Move** and **Rotate**, as well as the arrow keys.

- You cannot use any tools that utilize the copy feature, like **Copy**, **Mirror**, and **Offset**.

### How To: Move a View on a Sheet

1. Open a sheet view.
2. Select and drag a view to another location on the sheet. When selecting the view, the view title moves with the view.

### How To: Modify the Viewport's View Title

1. Open a sheet view.
2. Select only the view title and drag it to the new location.

- To modify the length of the line under the title name, select the viewport and drag the controls, as shown in Figure 13–21.

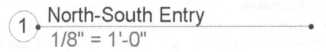

**Figure 13–21**

- To change the title of a view on a sheet without changing its name in the Project Browser, select either the viewport or the view title, then in Properties, in the *Identity Data* section, type a new title for the *Title on Sheet* parameter, as shown in Figure 13–22.

**Figure 13–22**

## Rotating Views

When creating a vertical sheet, you can rotate the view on the sheet by 90°. Select the view on the sheet and set the direction of rotation in the **Rotation on Sheet** drop-down list in the Options Bar, as shown in Figure 13–23.

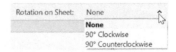

**Figure 13–23**

**Note:** *For more information about rotating the project or individual views to angles other than 90°, refer to the ASCENT guide Autodesk Revit: Site Planning and Design.*

## Working Inside Views

To make small changes to a view while working on a sheet:

- Double-click *inside* the view to activate it.
- Double-click *outside* the view to deactivate it.

Only elements in the viewport are available for modification. The rest of the sheet is grayed out, as shown in Figure 13–24.

- Use this method only for small changes. Significant changes should be made directly in the view.

**Figure 13–24**

- You can activate and deactivate views by selecting the viewport, right-clicking, and selecting from the menu, or by using the tools found in the *Modify | Viewports* or *Views* tab>Sheet Composition panel.

- Changes you make to elements when a view is activated also display in the original view.

- If you are unsure which sheet a view is on, right-click on the view in the Project Browser and select **Open Sheet**. This is not available for schedules and legends, which can be placed on more than one sheet.

# Resizing Views on Sheets

Each view displays the extents of the model or the elements contained in the crop region. If the view does not fit on a sheet (as shown in Figure 13–25), you might need to crop the view or move the elevation markers closer to the building.

**Figure 13–25**

*Note: If the extents of the view change dramatically based on a scale change or a crop region, it is easier to delete the view on the sheet and drag it over again.*

- For information about laying out views on sheets using guide grids, see *B.1 Pressure Loss Reports*.

- For information about working with revisions in views and on sheets, see *B.3 Revision Tracking*.

## How To: Add an Image to a Sheet

Company logos and renderings saved to image files (such as .JPG and .PNG) can be added directly on a sheet or in a view.

1. In the *Insert* tab>Import panel, click ![icon] (Image).

2. In the Import Image dialog box, select and open the image file. The extents of the image display, as shown in Figure 13–26.

**Figure 13–26**

3. Place the image where you want it.

4. The image is displayed. Pick one of the grips and extend it to modify the size of the image.

- In Properties, you can adjust the height and width and also set the *Draw Layer* to either **Background** or **Foreground**, as shown in Figure 13–27.

| Dimensions | ≫ |
|---|---|
| Width | 1' 5 185/256" |
| Height | 1' 1 41/64" |
| Horizontal Scale | 1.000000 |
| Vertical Scale | 1.000000 |
| Lock Proportions | ☑ |
| Other | ≫ |
| Draw Layer | Background |

**Figure 13–27**

- You can select more than one image at a time and move them as a group to the background or foreground.

- In the *Modify | Raster Images* tab (shown in Figure 13–28), you can access the Arrange options and the **Manage Images** command.

**Figure 13–28**

# Practice 13a
# Set Up Sheets - All Disciplines

## Practice Objectives

- Set up project properties.
- Create sheets individually.
- Move a view aligned to another sheet.
- Modify views to prepare them to be placed on sheets.
- Place views on sheets.

In this practice, you will complete the project information, add new sheets and use existing sheets. You will fill in title block information and then add views to sheets, such as the Lighting Plan sheet shown in Figure 13-29. Complete as many sheets as you have time for.

**Figure 13-29**

## Task 1:  Complete the project information.

1.  In the practice files *Working Models>General* folder, open **Gen-Sheets.rvt**.

2.  In the *Manage* tab>Settings panel, click 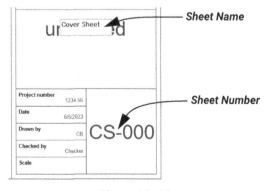 (Project Information).

3.  In the Project Properties dialog box, add the following values:

    *   *Project Issue Date:* **Today's date**
    *   *Project Status:* **Design Development**
    *   *Client Name:* **ASCENT School District**
    *   *Project Name:* **Elementary School**
    *   *Project Number:* **1234.56**

    *Note: These values are added automatically to any sheet you create.*

4.  Click **OK** and save the project.

## Task 2:  Create a cover sheet, import an image, and modify the title block.

1.  In the *View* tab>Sheet Composition panel, click (Sheet).

2.  In the New Sheet dialog box, select the **ASCENT 22 x 34 Horizontal** title block.

3.  Click **OK**.

4.  Zoom in on the lower-right corner of the title block. The Project Properties filled out earlier are automatically added to the sheet (e.g., Project number, Project Status, etc.).

5.  Continue filling out the title block by changing *unnamed* to **Cover Sheet** and the sheet number to **CS-000**, as shown in Figure 13–30.

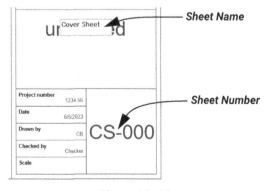

Figure 13–30

6.  Set *Drawn by* to your initials. Leave the *Checked by* and *Date* parameters as is.

    *Note: The Scale is empty because this will be automatically entered when a view is inserted onto a sheet. If a sheet has multiple scales, the scale reads **As Indicated**.*

7. In the Project Browser, expand the *Sheets (all)* node. Note that the sheet you created is now in the list of sheets.

8. Open another sheet. The project parameter values are repeated but note that the *Drawn By* value is not added because it is a parameter that is set per sheet.

9. Go back to the **CS-000 - Cover Sheet** and type **ZA** to zoom out and display the whole sheet.

10. In the *Insert* tab>Import panel, click ▣ (Import Image).

    • Note: If the image is one that might change, you would use the **Link Image** command so it can be updated through the Manage Links dialog box when required.

11. In the Import Image dialog box, navigate to the practice files *Images* folder and select **School Perspective.jpg**.

12. Click **Open**.

13. Your cursor will have an X shape (indicating the size of your image). Click to place the image on the sheet.

14. Click ▧ (Modify).

15. Use the grips to adjust the size of the image so it is smaller and move it into the upper left corner of the sheet, as shown in Figure 13–31, to make room for notes.

**Figure 13–31**

16. In the Project Browser, right-click on *Sheets (all)* and select **New Sheet...**.

17. In the New Sheet dialog box, select the title block **ASCENT 30x42 Horizontal** and click **OK**.

18. Select the titleblock and in the Type Selector, select **ASCENT 22 x 34 Horizontal**. Note that the title block changes.

19. With the title block still selected, in Properties, in the *Identity Data* section, change the *Sheet Name* to **Electrical Details** and *Sheet Number* to **E-002**.

20. Click in an empty area in the view. Note that the title block information updates on the sheet.

21. Save the project.

## Task 3: Duplicate a sheet, and add and modify views.

1. In the Project Browser, right-click on **CS-000 - Cover Sheet** and select **Duplicate Sheet>Duplicate Empty Sheet**.

2. In the Project Browser, right-click on the new sheet and select **Rename...**.

3. In the Sheet Title dialog box, set the *Number* to **G-001** and the *Name* to **School Perspective View**.

4. Click **OK**. The sheet updates with the information.

5. In the Project Browser, from the *Coordination>MEP>3D Views* section, drag and drop the **3D - School Perspective View** view onto the upper right side of the sheet, as shown in Figure 13–32.

**Figure 13–32**

6. Select the edge of the viewport. In the Type Selector, select **Viewport: NoTitle**.

7. Double-click inside the viewport; the titleblock grays out and you can modify the actual view.

8. In Properties, in the *Extents* section, clear the check from **Crop Region Visible**. (This could also be done in the View Control Bar.)

9. Double-click outside the viewport to deactivate the view and return to the sheet.

10. Select the perspective view, right-click, and select **Move Aligned to Sheet...**, as shown in Figure 13–33.

**Figure 13–33**

11. In the Select Sheet dialog box, select **Sheet: CS-000 - Cover Sheet** and click **OK**. The persecutive view is no longer displayed on the sheet.

12. Open the **CS-000 Cover Sheet** and note that the 3D perspective view is now on the sheet in the upper right corner or in the location you placed it on the original sheet.

13. In the Project Browser, right-click on **M-102 - 01 Mechanical Schematic** and select **Duplicate Sheet>Duplicate with Views**, as shown in Figure 13-34.

Figure 13-34

14. In the Duplicate with Views dialog box, select **Duplicate**.

15. The sheet opens. Note that the new sheet number (in this example **M-103**, as shown in Figure 13-35) follows the sequence from the duplicated sheet (M-102). The sheet name will have **Copy** and a number added after the name, as shown in Figure 13-35.

Figure 13-35

*Note: You can change the sheet number and name in the title block or by renaming it in the Project Browser.*

16. Rename the sheet **01 Mechanical Plan - Area A**.

17. In the Project Browser, in the *Mechanical>HVAC>Floor Plans* section, note that there is now a **01 Mechanical Schematic Copy 1.** This was created when selecting **Duplicate with Views**. Note: This is useful if you need to modify the view but do not want to modify the original view.

18. With sheet **M-103 - 01 Mechanical - Area A** the active view, select the view on the sheet.

19. In the *Modify | Viewports* tab>Positioning & View panel, expand the floor plan, as shown in Figure 13–36, and select **Floor Plan : 01 Mechanical Plan - Area A**. The view updates.

**Figure 13–36**

20. In the Project Browser, right-click on sheet **E-101 - 01 Electrical Plan** and select **Duplicate Sheet>Duplicate with Views**.

21. In the Duplicate with Views dialog box, select **Duplicate as a dependent**.

22. A copy of the 01 Electrical plan sheet opens with a copy of the 01 Electrical Plan view as **01 Lighting Plan - Dependent 1** view.

23. Rename just the sheet name to **01 Electrical North/South Wing Plan**.

24. In the Project Browser, expand **Electrical>Lighting>Floor Plans>01 Lighting Plan** and note that there is a dependent copy of the view. Rename the dependent view to **01 Lighting Plan - North Wing**.

25. Right-click on the **01 Lighting Plan** view and select **Duplicate Views>Duplicate as Dependent**. Create another dependent view of the 01 Lighting Plan view.

26. Name the dependent view **01 Lighting Plan - South Wing**.

**27.** Open the **01 Lighting Plan - North Wing** view, zoom out to see the crop region (toggle it on, if needed), and resize it to fit the north classroom wing, as shown in Figure 13–37.

**Figure 13–37**

**28.** Toggle the crop region off.

**29.** Repeat the steps with the **01 Lighting Plan - South Wing** view.

**30.** Open the **E-102 - 01 Electrical North/South Wing Plan** sheet.

**31.** Because the view's crop region was adjusted, you now need to adjust the view title. Select just the view title and move the view title closer to the north wing view. Click in an empty area in the view.

**32.** Select the view. Using the view title grip, drag the view title's extension line in to align with the view.

**33.** From the Project Browser, drag and drop the **1st Floor Lighting Plan South Wing** view you just created onto the sheet.

**34.** Save and close the project.

**End of practice**

# 13.5 Printing Sheets

With the **Print** command, you can print individual sheets or a list of selected sheets. You can also print an individual view or a portion of a view for check prints or presentations. To open the Print dialog box (shown in Figure 13–38), in the *File* tab, click 🖶 (Print), or press <Ctrl>+<P>.

**Figure 13–38**

## Printing Options

The Print dialog box is divided into the following areas: *Printer, File, Print Range, Options,* and *Settings*. Modify them as needed to produce the plot you want.

- **Printing Tips**: Opens Autodesk WikiHelp online, in which you can find help with troubleshooting printing issues.

- **Preview**: Opens a preview of the print output so that you can see what is going to be printed.

# Printer

Select from the list of available printers, as shown in Figure 13–39. Click **Properties...** to adjust the properties of the selected printer. The options vary according to the printer. Select the **Print to file** option to print to a file rather than directly to a printer. You can create .PLT or .PRN files.

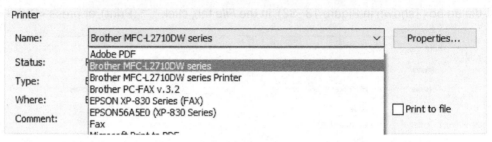

**Figure 13–39**

- You must have a PDF print driver installed on your system to print to PDF, or you can export views and sheets to PDF.

# File

The *File* area is only available if the **Print to file** option has been selected in the *Printer* area or if you are printing to an electronic-only type of printer. You can create one file or multiple files depending on the type of printer you are using, as shown in Figure 13–40. Click **Browse...** to select the file location and name.

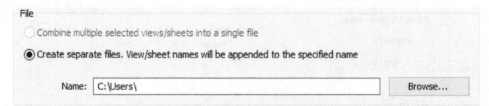

**Figure 13–40**

# Print Range

The *Print Range* area enables you to print individual views/sheets or sets of views/sheets, as shown in Figure 13–41.

Figure 13–41

- **Current window:** Prints the entire current sheet or view you have open.

- **Visible portion of current window:** Prints only what is displayed in the current sheet or view.

- **Selected views/sheets:** Prints multiple views or sheets. Click **Select...** to open the Select Views/Sheets dialog box (shown in Figure 13–42) to choose what to include in the print set. You can save these sets by name so that you can more easily print the same group again.

Figure 13–42

- You can edit the selected views and sheets by **Browser organization**, **Sheet Number (Ascending)**, or **Manual order**. If you select **Manual order**, you can drag the views and sheets to put them in a custom order, as shown in Figure 13–43.

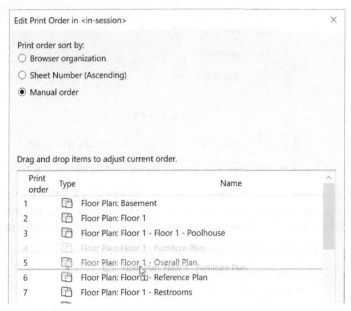

**Figure 13–43**

## Options

If your printer supports multiple copies, you can specify the number in the *Options* area, as shown in Figure 13–44. You can also reverse the print order or collate your prints. These options are also available in the printer properties.

**Figure 13–44**

# Settings

Click **Setup...** to open the Print Setup dialog box, as shown in Figure 13–45. Here, you can specify the *Orientation* and *Zoom* settings, among others. You can also save these settings by name.

**Figure 13–45**

- In the *Options* area, specify the types of elements you want to print or not print. Unless specified, all of the elements in a view or sheet print.

- Sheets should always be printed at **Zoom** set to **100%** size unless you are creating a quick markup set that does not need to be exact.

# Export Views and Sheets to PDF

If you do not have a PDF driver to utilize in the Print dialog box, you can export your views or sheets to PDF. If you set the *Export Range* to **Selected views/sheets**, you have the ability to edit the print order of the views/sheets by **Browser organization**, **Sheet Number (Ascending)**, or **Manual order**.

## How To: Export Views and Sheets to PDF

1.  In the File menu, select ▣ (Export)> ▤ (PDF).

2.  In the PDF Export dialog box (shown in Figure 13–46), enter a *File Name* and the *Location* you would like the PDF to be exported to, and select the other settings, as needed.

    *   The PDF Export settings are similar to those found in the Revit Print dialog box.

**Figure 13–46**

3.  Click **Export**.

# Chapter Review Questions

1. How do you specify the size of a sheet?

   a. In the Sheet Properties, specify the **Sheet Size**.

   b. In the Options Bar, specify the **Sheet Size**.

   c. In the New Sheet dialog box, select a title block to control the Sheet Size.

   d. In the Sheet view, right-click and select **Sheet Size**.

2. How is the title block information filled in, as shown in Figure 13–47? (Select all that apply.)

**Figure 13–47**

   a. Select the title block and select the label that you want to change.

   b. Select the title block and modify it in Properties.

   c. Right-click on the sheet in the Project Browser and select **Information**.

   d. Some of the information is filled in automatically from the Project Information.

3. On how many sheets can a floor plan view be placed?

   a. 1

   b. 2-5

   c. 6+

   d. As many as you want

4. Which of the following is the best method to use if the size of a view is too large for a sheet, as shown in Figure 13–48?

**Figure 13–48**

a. Delete the view, change the scale, and place the view back on the sheet.

b. Change the scale of the sheet.


5. How do you set up a view on a sheet that only displays part of a floor plan?

a. Drag and drop the view to the sheet and use the crop region to modify it.

b. Activate the view and rescale it.

c. Create a callout view displaying the part that you want to use and place the callout view on the sheet.

d. Open the view in the Project Browser and change the View Scale.


6. You can only export sheets to PDF.

a. True

b. False

# Command Summary

| Button | Command | Location |
|--------|---------|----------|
| | **Activate View** | • **Ribbon:** *(select the view) Modify | Viewports* tab> Viewport panel<br>• **Double-click:** *(in viewport)*<br>• **Right-click:** *(on view)* Activate View |
| | **Deactivate View** | • **Ribbon:** *View* tab>Sheet Composition panel, expand Viewports<br>• **Double-click:** *(on sheet)*<br>• **Right-click:** *(on view)* Deactivate View |
| | **PDF** | • *File* **tab**>Export |
| | **Place View** | • **Ribbon:** *View* tab>Sheet Composition panel |
| | **Print** | • *File* **tab** |
| | **Sheet** | • **Ribbon:** *View* tab>Sheet Composition panel |

# Working with Annotations

When you create construction documents, annotations are essential for showing the design intent. Annotations such as dimensions and text can be added to views at any time during the creation of a project. Detail lines and symbols can also be added to views as you create the working drawing, while legends can be created to provide a place to document any symbols that are used in a project.

## Learning Objectives

- Add dimensions to the model as a part of the working drawings.
- Add text to a view and use leaders to create notes pointing to a specific part of the model.
- Create text types using different fonts and sizes to suit your company standards.
- Draw detail lines to further enhance the documentation view.
- Add view-specific annotation symbols for added clarity.
- Create legend views and populate them with symbols of elements in the project.

# 14.1 Working with Dimensions

You can create permanent dimensions using aligned, linear, angular, radial, diameter, and arc length dimensions. These can be individual or a string of dimensions, as shown in Figure 14–1. With aligned dimensions, you can also dimension entire walls with openings, grid lines, and/or intersecting walls.

**Figure 14–1**

- Dimensions referencing model elements must be added to the model in a view. You can dimension on sheets, but only to items added directly on the sheets.

- Dimensions are available in the *Annotate* tab>Dimension panel (shown in Figure 14–2) and in the *Modify* tab>Measure panel.

**Figure 14–2**

**Note:** (Aligned) is also located in the Quick Access Toolbar.

- Dimensions can be added to isometric 3D views whether they are locked or not. Proceed with caution when selecting the items to dimension. You can set the work plane or use <Tab> to cycle through elements.

- Ensure that the witness lines and text orientation is snapping to and extending in the correct direction as intended.

## How To: Add Aligned Dimensions with Options

1. Start the ⟍ (Aligned) command or type **DI**.

2. In the Type Selector, select a dimension style.

3. In the Options Bar, select the location line of the wall to dimension from, as shown in Figure 14-3.

   • This option can be changed as you add dimensions.

Figure 14-3

   • Most MEP fixtures have alignment lines along their centerline. You can also dimension to individual parts of components, as shown in Figure 14-4.

Figure 14-4

4.  In the Options Bar, select your preference from the Pick drop-down list:

    • **Individual References:** Select the elements in order (as shown in Figure 14–5) and then click in an empty space in the view to position the dimension string.

**Figure 14–5**

## How To: Add Other Types of Dimensions

1.  In the *Annotate* tab>Dimension panel, select a dimension method.

| | | |
|---|---|---|
| | **Aligned** | Most commonly used dimension type. Select individual elements or entire walls to dimension. |
| | **Linear** | Used when you need to specify certain points on elements. |
| | **Angular** | Used to dimension the angle between two elements. |
| | **Radial** | Used to dimension the radius of circular elements. |
| | **Diameter** | Used to dimension the diameter of circular elements. |
| | **Arc Length** | Used to dimension the length of the arc of circular elements. |

*Note: The dimension methods are also accessible in the Modify | Place Dimensions tab> Dimension panel when any of the dimension commands are active.*

2.  In the Type Selector, select the dimension type.
3.  Follow the prompts for the selected method.

# Modifying Dimensions

When you move elements that are dimensioned (e.g., a wall), the dimensions automatically update. You can also modify dimensions by selecting a dimension or dimension string and making changes. Figure 14-6 shows the various parts of dimensions that aid in modifying.

**Figure 14-6**

- To move the dimension text, select the **Drag text** control under the text and drag it to a new location. It automatically creates a leader from the dimension line if you drag it away. The style of the leader (arc or line) depends on the dimension style.

- To move the dimension line (the line parallel to the element being dimensioned), simply drag the line to a new location, or select the dimension and drag the ⁺⁺⁺ (Drag to new position) control.

- To change the gap between the witness line and the element being dimensioned, drag the control at the end of the witness line.

- To move the witness line (the line perpendicular to the element being dimensioned) to a different element or face of a wall, use the **Move Witness Line** control in the middle of the witness line. While moving the witness line, you can hover your cursor over a element or component and press <Tab> repeatedly to cycle through the various options. You can also drag this control to move the witness line to a different element, or right-click on the control and select **Move Witness Line**.

## Adding and Deleting Dimensions in a String

- To add a witness line to a string of dimensions, select the dimension and, in the *Modify |
  Dimensions* tab>Witness Lines panel, click ⌐̶ (Edit Witness Lines). Select the element(s)
  you want to add to the dimension, as shown in Figure 14–7. Click in an empty space in the
  view to finish.

**Figure 14–7**

- To delete a witness line, drag the **Move Witness Line** control to a nearby witness line's
  element. Alternatively, you can hover the cursor over the control, right-click, and select
  **Delete Witness Line**.

- To delete one dimension in a string and break the string into two separate dimensions,
  select the string, hover your cursor over the dimension that you want to delete, and press
  <Tab>. When it highlights (as shown on the left in Figure 14–8), pick it and press <Delete>.
  The selected dimension is deleted and the dimension string is separated into two elements,
  as shown on the right in Figure 14–8.

**Figure 14–8**

# Modifying the Dimension Text

Because Revit is parametric, changing the dimension text without changing the elements dimensioned would cause problems throughout the project. These issues could cause problems beyond the model if you use the project model to estimate materials or work with other disciplines.

You can append the existing dimension text with prefixes and suffixes (as shown in Figure 14–9), or create a dimension style that has a prefix or suffix preset in the Type Properties. This can help you in renovation projects.

Figure 14–9

Double-click on the dimension text to open the Dimension Text dialog box, as shown in Figure 14–10, and make modifications as needed.

Figure 14–10

## Hint: Multiple Dimension Options

If you are creating details that show one element with multiple dimension values, as shown in Figure 14–11, you can easily modify the dimension text.

**Figure 14–11**

Select the dimension and then the dimension text. The Dimension Text dialog box opens. You can replace the text, as shown in Figure 14–12, or add text fields above or below, as well as a prefix or suffix.

**Figure 14–12**

- This also works with Equality Text Labels.

If you find that you are always modifying dimensions manually, you can create a type-driven dimension style by duplicating the dimension style and specifying a set prefix and suffix within the type parameters, as shown in Figure 14–13.

**Figure 14–13**

This eliminates the need to manually modify the dimension every time you need to add a prefix or suffix.

# Setting Constraints

The three types of constraints that work with dimensions are locks and equal settings, as shown in Figure 14–14, as well as labels.

**Figure 14–14**

## Locking Dimensions

When you lock a dimension, the value is set and you cannot make a change between it and the referenced elements. If it is unlocked, you can move it and change its value.

Note that when you use this and move an element, any elements that are locked to the dimension also move.

## Setting Dimensions Equal

For a string of dimensions, select the **EQ** symbol to constrain the elements to be at an equal distance apart. This actually moves the elements that are dimensioned.

- The equality text display can be changed in Properties, as shown in Figure 14–15. The style for each of the display types is set in the dimension type.

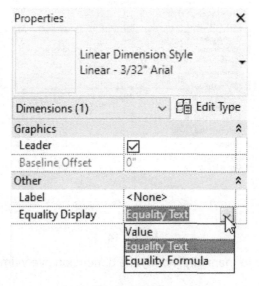

**Figure 14–15**

## Labeling Dimensions

If you have a distance that needs to be repeated multiple times, such as the *Wall to AT* label shown in Figure 14–16, or one where you want to use a formula based on another dimension, you can create and apply a global parameter, also called a label, to the dimension.

**Figure 14–16**

- To apply an existing label to a dimension, select the dimension and in the *Modify | Dimensions* tab>Label Dimension panel, select the label in the drop-down list, as shown in Figure 14–17.

**Figure 14–17**

## How To: Create a Label

1. Select a dimension.

2. In the *Modify | Dimensions* tab>Label Dimension panel, click 🖹 (Create Parameter).

3. In the Global Parameter Properties dialog box, type in a *Name*, as shown in Figure 14–18, and click **OK**.

**Figure 14–18**

4. The label is applied to the dimension.

## How To: Edit the Label Information

1. Select a labeled dimension.

2. Click ✎ (Global Parameters), as shown in Figure 14–19.

**Figure 14–19**

3.  In the Global Parameters dialog box, in the *Value* column, type the new distance, as shown in Figure 14–20.

**Figure 14–20**

4.  Click **OK**. The selected dimension and any other dimensions using the same label are updated.

*   You can also edit, create, and delete global parameters in this dialog box.

# Working with Constraints

To find out which elements have constraints applied to them, in the View Control Bar, click

 (Reveal Constraints). Constraints display as shown in Figure 14–21.

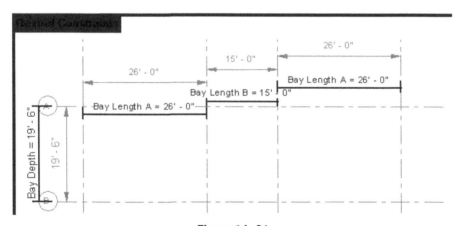

**Figure 14–21**

- If you try to move the element beyond the appropriate constraints, a warning dialog box displays, as shown in Figure 14–22.

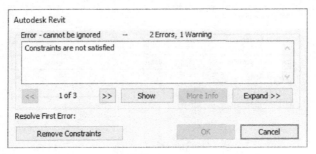

**Figure 14–22**

- If you delete dimensions that are constrained, a warning dialog box displays, as shown in Figure 14–23. Click **OK** to retain the constraint or click **Unconstrain** to remove the constraint.

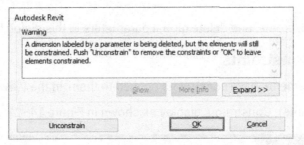

**Figure 14–23**

# Practice 14a
# Work with Dimensions - Mechanical

## Practice Objectives

- Add a string of dimensions.
- Modify the dimension string.

In this practice, you will add and modify dimensions for a mechanical floor plan view.

1. In the practice files *Working Models>Mechanical* folder, open **Mech-Dimensions.rvt**.

2. Open the Mechanical>HVAC>Floor Plans>**01 Mechanical Plan** view and zoom in on the upper-left corner of the north wing.

3. In the *Annotate* tab>Dimension panel, click ✎ (Aligned).

4. In the Options Bar, verify that the **Wall centerlines** option is selected.

5. Dimension the first four duct branches (not the diffusers or the flex duct), starting from the left side wall to the rightmost branch in the two rooms, as shown in Figure 14–24.

   - Hint: While dimensioning, press <Tab> to select the center of the duct branches.

**Figure 14–24**

6. Click ▹ (Modify).

7. Select the dimension, then select the **Move Witness Line** control on the far left, as shown in Figure 14–25.

8. Drag the control towards the interior side of the wall and press <Tab>. When the inside of the wall highlights, release the left mouse button to place the witness line, as shown in Figure 14–26.

Figure 14–25                                           Figure 14–26

9. Click ⌖ (Modify).

10. Select the far right duct branch, as shown in Figure 14–27.

11. The corresponding dimension text turns blue. Select the dimension and change its value from **12'** to **10'**. The duct branch and the flex ductwork move accordingly, but the air terminal maintains its original position, as shown in Figure 14–27.

Figure 14–27

12. Click ⌖ (Modify) and select the dimension line.

13. In the *Modify | Dimensions* tab>Witness Lines panel, click ⊢⊣ (Edit Witness Lines).

**14.** Select the center of the wall to add a fifth dimension to the string of dimensions. Click in an empty space in the view away from any objects to place the new dimension. Figure 14–28 shows the new dimension added to the dimension string. Add more dimensions, as needed.

**Figure 14–28**

**15.** Click  (Modify).

**16.** Save and close the project.

**End of practice**

# Practice 14b
# Work with Dimensions - Electrical

## Practice Objectives

- Add a string of dimensions.
- Modify the dimension string.

In this practice, you will add and modify dimensions.

1. In the practice files *Working Models>Electrical* folder, open **Elec-Dimensions.rvt**.

2. Open the Electrical>Power>Floor Plans>**01 Power Plan** view and zoom in on the upper-left corner of the north wing.

3. In the *Annotate* tab>Dimension panel, click ⟍ (Aligned).

4. In the Options Bar, verify that the **Wall centerlines** option is selected.

5. Dimension the location of the receptacles at their connection points in the first two classrooms, starting from the left side wall and including the other walls, as shown in Figure 14–29.

**Figure 14–29**

6. Select the **Move Witness Line** control on the far left, as shown in Figure 14–30.

7. Drag the control towards the interior side of the wall and press <Tab>. When the inside of the wall highlights, release the left mouse button to place the witness line, as shown in Figure 14–31.

| Figure 14–30 | Figure 14–31 |

8.  Repeat the process and move the witness lines at the center of the interior walls to the left side of the walls.

9.  In the *Modify | Dimensions* tab>Witness Lines panel, click ⊢┤ (Edit Witness Lines).

10. Add another dimension to the right side of both interior walls (press <Tab> to select the outer edge rather than the default alignment of center), as shown for the second wall in Figure 14–32. Click in an empty space in the view away from any objects to add the new dimension.

**2' - 4 5/32"**

**Figure 14–32**

11. Select the dimension string and click and drag the **Drag Text** control to move some of the text so you can read each number. Figure 14–33 shows the overlapping dimensions dragged up above the dimension line.

*Drag Text control*

2' - 4 5/32"     0' - 4"

11' - 7 27/32"     11' - 2 3/4"

**Figure 14–33**

12. Click ⃗ (Modify).

**13.** Select one of the receptacles. The corresponding dimension text turns blue. Select the dimension and change its value to **3'-6"**, as shown in Figure 14–34. The receptacle moves.

**Figure 14–34**

**14.** Click in an empty area in the view to release the selection.

**15.** Make any other changes to the dimensions that you may want, as shown in Figure 14–35.

**Figure 14–35**

**16.** Save and close the project.

**End of practice**

# Practice 14c
# Work with Dimensions - Plumbing

## Practice Objectives

- Add a string of dimensions.
- Modify the dimension string.

In this practice, you will add and modify dimensions.

1. In the practice files *Working Models>Plumbing* folder, open **Plumb-Dimensions.rvt**.
2. Open the Plumbing>Plumbing>Floor Plans>**01 Plumbing Plan** view and zoom in on one of the restrooms near the gym.
3. In the *Annotate* tab>Dimension panel, click ⤡ (Aligned).
4. In the Options Bar, verify that the **Wall centerlines** is selected.
5. Dimension the location of the center of the lavatories, as shown in Figure 14–36.

Dimension to the center of the sinks

**Figure 14–36**

6. Select the **Move Witness Line** control (shown in Figure 14–37) on the dimension that is dimensioning to the center of the wall.

7. Drag the control towards the interior side of the wall and press <Tab>. When the inside of the wall highlights, release the left mouse button to place the witness line, as shown in Figure 14–38.

**Figure 14–37**        **Figure 14–38**

8. Click ⬚ (Modify) and select the top lavatory closest to the restroom exit.

9. The corresponding dimension text turns blue. Select the dimension text and change its value to **4'-0"**. You get an error that the family is connected to a network, as shown in Figure 14–39. Click **Cancel**.

**Figure 14–39**

• Note that it is not advisable to modify the location of fixtures once you have connected piping to them.

**10.** Select the dimension string and click and drag the **Drag Text** control to move some of the text so you can read each number. Figure 14-40 shows the overlapping dimensions dragged up above the dimension line.

**Figure 14-40**

**11.** Save and close the project.

**End of practice**

# 14.2 Working with Text

The **Text** command enables you to add notes to views or sheets, such as the detail shown in Figure 14–41. The same command is used to create text with or without leaders.

1. All ductwork shown on plans shall be concealed above ceiling or in walls unless noted otherwise.
2. All duct dimensions are in inches and are inside clear.
3. All branch duct runouts to diffusers shall be full connection size of diffuser, unless noted otherwise.

**Figure 14–41**

The text height is automatically set by the text type in conjunction with the scale of the view (as shown in Figure 14–42, using the same size text type at two different scales). Text types display at the specified height, both in the views and on the sheet.

Turning Vanes at Elbows with Flow Greater Than 475 L/s; Typical

Return Air to Return Plenum (Provide Volume Damper); Typical

Return Air Plenum

*Scale: 1/8"=1'-0"*

*Scale: 1/4"=1'-0"*

**Figure 14–42**

## How To: Add Text

1. In the Quick Access Toolbar or *Annotate* tab>Text panel, click $\mathbf{A}$ (Text).

2. In the Type Selector, set the text type.

   *Note: The text type sets the font and height of the text.*

3. In the *Modify | Place Text* tab>Leader panel, select the method you want to use: $\mathbf{A}$ (No Leader), ↞A (One Segment), ⟋A (Two Segments), or ⌒A (Curved).

4. In the Alignment panel, set the overall justification for the text and leader, as shown in Figure 14–43.

**Figure 14–43**

5. Select the location for the leader and text.

   - Use alignment lines to help you align the text with other text elements.

   - If **No leader** is selected, select the start point for the text and begin typing.

   - If using a leader, the first point places the arrow and you then select points for the leader. The text starts at the last leader point.

   - To set a word wrapping distance, click and drag the circle grip controls to set the start and end points of the text.

6. Type the needed text. In the *Edit Text* tab, specify additional options for the font and paragraph, as shown in Figure 14–44.

**Figure 14–44**

7. In the *Edit Text* tab>Edit Text panel, click ☒ (Close) or click outside the text box to complete the text element.

   - Pressing <Enter> after a line of text starts a new line of text in the same text window.

## How To: Add Text Symbols

1.  Start the **Text** command and click to place the text.

2.  As you are typing text and need to insert a symbol, right-click and select **Symbols** from the shortcut menu. Select from the list of commonly used symbols, as shown in Figure 14–45.

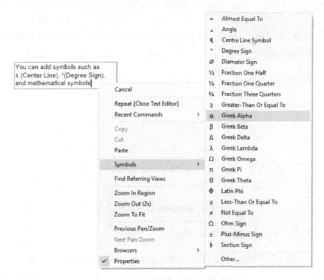

**Figure 14–45**

3.  If the symbol you need is not listed, click **Other...**.

4.  In the Character Map dialog box, click on a symbol and click **Select**, as shown in Figure 14–46.

**Figure 14–46**

5. Click **Copy** to copy the character to the clipboard and paste it into the text box.

- The font in the Character Map should match the font used by the text type. You do not want to use a different font for symbols.

# Editing Text

Editing text notes takes place at two levels:

- Modifying the text note, which includes the **Leader** and **Paragraph** styles.

- Editing the text, which includes changes to individual letters, words, and paragraphs in the text note.

## Modifying the Text Note

Click once on the text note to modify the text box and leaders using controls, as shown in Figure 14−47, or using the tools in the *Modify | Text Notes* tab.

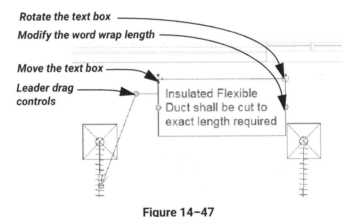

**Figure 14−47**

---

### How To: Add a Leader to Text Notes

---

1. Select the text note.

2. In the *Modify | Text Notes* tab>Leader panel, select the direction and justification for the new leader, as shown in Figure 14−48.

**Figure 14−48**

3. The leader is applied, as shown in Figure 14–49. Use the drag controls to place the arrow as needed.

**Figure 14–49**

- You can remove leaders by clicking ⁻A (Remove Last Leader).

## Editing the Text

The *Edit Text* tab enables you to make various customizations. These include modifying the font of selected words as well as creating bulleted and numbered lists, as shown in Figure 14–50.

<u>General Notes</u>
1. Notify designer of intention to start construction at least 10 days prior to start of site work.
2. Installer shall provide the following:
   - 24-hour notice of start of construction
   - Inspection of bottom of bed or covering required by state inspector
   - All environmental management inspection sheets must be emailed to designer's office within 24 hours of inspection.

**Figure 14–50**

- You can **Cut**, **Copy,** and **Paste** text using the clipboard. For example, you can copy text from a document and then paste it into the text editor in Revit.

- To help you see the text better as you are modifying it, in the *Edit Text* tab, expand the Edit Text panel and select one or both of the options, as shown in Figure 14–51.

**Figure 14–51**

## How To: Modify the Font

1. Select individual letters or words.

2. Click on the font modification you want to include:

| | | | |
|---|---|---|---|
| **B** | (Bold) | $X_2$ | (Subscript) |
| *I* | (Italic) | $X^2$ | (Superscript) |
| <u>U</u> | (Underline) | ᵃA | (All Caps) |

- When pasting text from a document outside of Revit, font modifications (e.g, Bold, Italic, etc.) are retained.

## How To: Create Lists

1. In Edit Text mode, place the cursor in the line where you want to add to a list.

2. In the *Edit Text* tab>Paragraph panel, click the type of list you want to create:

| | | | |
|---|---|---|---|
| ☰ | (Bullets) | ☰ | (Uppercase Letters) |
| ☰ | (Numbers) | ☰ | (Lowercase Letters) |

3. As you type, press <Enter> and the next line in the list is incremented.

   **Note:** *If you do not want a line to be a part of the list, select the line and click* None *(None) on the Paragraph panel.*

4. To include sub-lists, at the beginning of the next line, click 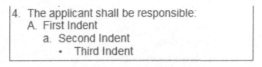 (Increase Indent) or press <Tab>. This indents the line and applies the next level of lists, as shown in Figure 14–52.

> 4. The applicant shall be responsible:
>    A. First Indent
>       a. Second Indent
>          • Third Indent

**Figure 14–52**

*Note: The indent distance is set up by the text type Tab Size.*

- You can change the type of list after you have applied the first increment. For example, you might want to use a list of bullets instead of letters, as shown in Figure 14–53.

5. Click 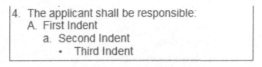 (Decrease Indent) or press <Shift>+<Tab> to return to the previous list style.

- Press <Shift>+<Enter> to create a blank line in a numbered list.

- To create columns or other separate text boxes that build on a numbering system (as shown in Figure 14–53), create the second text box and list, then place the cursor on one of the lines and in the Paragraph panel, click (Increment List Value) until the list matches the next number in the sequence.

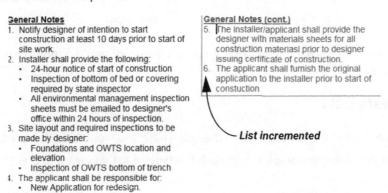

**General Notes**
1. Notify designer of intention to start construction at least 10 days prior to start of site work.
2. Installer shall provide the following:
   - 24-hour notice of start of construction
   - Inspection of bottom of bed or covering required by state inspector
   - All environmental management inspection sheets must be emailed to designer's office within 24 hours of inspection.
3. Site layout and required inspections to be made by designer:
   - Foundations and OWTS location and elevation
   - Inspection of OWTS bottom of trench
4. The applicant shall be responsible for:
   - New Application for redesign.

**General Notes (cont.)**
5. The installer/applicant shall provide the designer with materials sheets for all construction materiasl prior to designer issuing certificate of construction.
6. The applicant shall furnish the original application to the installer prior to start of constuction

**List incremented**

**Figure 14–53**

6. Click (Decrement List Value) to move back a number.

> ### 💡 Hint: Model Text
>
> Model text is different from annotation text. It is designed to create full-size text on the model itself. For example, you would use model text to create a sign on a door, as shown in Figure 14–54. One model text type is included with the default template. You can create other types as needed.

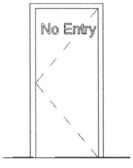

**Figure 14–54**

- Model text can be viewed in all views.
- Model text is added from the *Architecture* tab>Model panel by clicking 🅐 (Model Text).

# Spell Checking

The Check Spelling dialog box displays any misspelled words in context and provides several options for changing them, as shown in Figure 14–55.

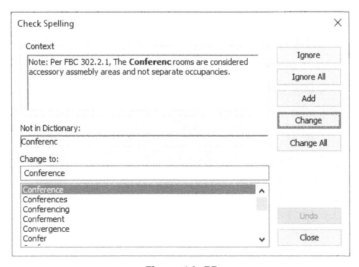

**Figure 14–55**

- Revit does not have active spell checking. It will only spell check when the command is activated.

- To spell check all text in a view, in the *Annotate* tab>Text panel, click <sup>ABC</sup> (Spelling), or press <F7>. As with other spell checkers, you can **Ignore**, **Add**, or **Change** the word.

- You can also check the spelling in selected text. With text selected, in the *Modify | Text Notes* tab>Tools panel, click <sup>ABC</sup> (Check Spelling).

# Creating Text Types

If you need new text types with a different text size or font (such as for a title or hand-lettering), you can create new ones, as shown in Figure 14–56. It is recommended that you create these in a project template so they are available in future projects.

## General Notes

1. This project consists of
furnishing and installing...

**Figure 14–56**

- You can copy and paste text types from one project to another or use **Transfer Project Standards**.

## How To: Create Text Types

1. In the *Annotate* tab>Text panel, click (Text Types).

   - Alternatively, start the **Text** command.

2. In Properties, click **Edit Type**.

3. In the Type Properties dialog box, click **Duplicate**.

4. In the Name dialog box, type a new name and click **OK**.

5. Modify the text parameters, as needed. The parameters are shown in Figure 14–57.

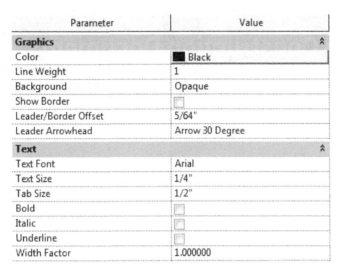

| Parameter | Value |
|---|---|
| **Graphics** | ⌃ |
| Color | ■ Black |
| Line Weight | 1 |
| Background | Opaque |
| Show Border | ☐ |
| Leader/Border Offset | 5/64" |
| Leader Arrowhead | Arrow 30 Degree |
| **Text** | ⌃ |
| Text Font | Arial |
| Text Size | 1/4" |
| Tab Size | 1/2" |
| Bold | ☐ |
| Italic | ☐ |
| Underline | ☐ |
| Width Factor | 1.000000 |

**Figure 14–57**

- The *Background* parameter can be set to **Opaque** or **Transparent**. An opaque background includes a masking region that hides lines or elements behind the text.

- In the *Text* area, the *Width Factor* parameter controls the width of the lettering, but does not affect the height. A width factor greater than **1** spreads the text out and a width factor less than **1** compresses it.

- The *Show Border* parameter, when selected, includes a rectangle around the text.

6. Click **OK** to close the Type Properties dialog box.

# Practice 14d
# Annotate Construction Documents – All Disciplines

## Practice Objective

- Add a bulleted list of general notes to a sheet.

In this practice, you will open a sheet and add general notes to it using the text command.

1. In the practice files *Working Models>General* folder, open **Gen-Text-Note.rvt**.

2. Open the sheet **CS-000 - Cover Sheet**.

3. Open a text editor such as Microsoft Word or Notepad.

4. Within the text editor software, open either **General Notes.docx** or **General Notes.txt** from the practice files *Documents* folder.

5. Copy the entire contents of the file to the clipboard (select all <Ctrl>+<A> and copy <Ctrl>+<C>).

6. In Revit, start the **Text** command. In the Quick Access Toolbar or *Annotate* tab>Text panel, click **A** (Text).

7. Verify that no leader is selected, set the text type to **3/32" Arial,** and draw a text box similar to the one shown in Figure 14–58.

**Figure 14–58**

8. In the *Edit Text* tab>Clipboard panel, click 🗐 (Paste).

9. Remain in Edit Text mode and zoom in on the text box. Note that there are numbered and lettered lists in the text but that they are not quite correct.

10. Select all of the text and in the *Edit Text* tab>Paragraph panel, click ☰ (List: Numbers).

- Depending on which document you opened and copied from, the paragraphs are recognized and numbered. If you copied from the .TXT file, the existing numbers and letters are still there. You will need to delete the existing numbering and modify the indents.

11. Select the paragraphs that were lettered in the original document and in the *Edit Text*

    tab>Paragraph panel, click ☰ (Increase Indent), then click ☰ (List: Lowercase letters) to change to a lettered list.

12. Select the numbered line and in the *Edit Text* tab>Paragraph panel, click ☰ (Increase Indent). If your number changes to a letter, click ☰ (List: Numbers).

13. Zoom in and remove the additional numbers and letters. Use **Increase Indent** or **Decrease Indent** to get the desired look, as shown in Figure 14–59.

1. General
   a. Existing ductwork and piping are shown only where necessary to establish relationship or connection points with new work. Not all existing ducts, pipes, and equipment are shown.
   b. For existing services at project site, verify exact size and location. Verify required clearances of equipment to new and existing material and electrical equipment.
   c. Raise, lower, remove, relocate or replace with new and reconnect to existing all piping and ductwork as required to maintain existing areas in operation during construction.
2. HVAC
   a. Examine architectural drawings to ensure that all ducts crossing fire and/or smoke separations are equipped with fire and/or smoke dampers. Notify the architect where additional dampers are required.
   b. Provide reheat coil transitions and transitions to smoke and/or fire dampers as required.
   c. Locate ceiling air outlets according to the architectural reflected ceiling plans. Confirm ceiling types shown on architectural drawings and install ceiling type supply and return or exhaust outlets to suit.
   d. All duct sizes show are inside clear dimensions.
3. Plumbing and Piping
   a. Verify exact invert elevation of points of connection to existing service prior to installation of new branch, mains or service relocation.
   b. Provide a valved drain at the low point in each piping system.
   c. Vent all high points in heating water and chilled water piping as specified.
   d. Provide condensate drip trap assemblies at the ends of steam mains, branches, and at all low points in the steam lines.
4. Electrical
   a. The electrical works shall comply with all the provisions in the Electrical Code and with consideration on the rules and regulations of local power company.
   b. Unless otherwise specified, wiring shall be done with PVC pipe.
   c. Electric meters installed by the power utility company are supplied and installed by the power utility company.
   d. The Electrical Code provides that only professional engineers can sign the electrical plans.
   e. Samples of materials to be used shall be submitted to the construction engineering office for approval before execution of the work.

**Figure 14–59**

14. At the beginning of the list, add the text **General Notes**. Make it bold and underlined, as shown in Figure 14–60.

15. Place the cursor at the end sentence of the **1. General** section. Hold <Shift> and press <Enter>. A new line is created without disrupting the numbering sequence.

16. Repeat this at the end of the discipline sections, as shown in Figure 14–60.

<u>General Notes</u>
1. General
    a. Existing ductwork and piping are shown only where necessary to establish relationship or connection points with new work. Not all existing ducts, pipes, and equipment are shown.
    b. For existing services at project site, verify exact size and location. Verify required clearances of equipment to new and existing material and electrical equipment.
    c. Raise, lower, remove, relocate or replace with new and reconnect to existing all piping and ductwork as required to maintain existing areas in operation during construction.

2. HVAC
    a. Examine architectural drawings to ensure that all ducts crossing fire and/or smoke separations are equipped with fire and/or smoke dampers. Notify the architect where additional dampers are required.
    b. Provide reheat coil transitions and transitions to smoke and/or fire dampers as required.
    c. Locate ceiling air outlets according to the architectural reflected ceiling plans. Confirm ceiling types shown on architectural drawings and install ceiling type supply and return or exhaust outlets to suit.
    d. All duct sizes show are inside clear dimensions.

3. Plumbing and Piping
    a. Verify exact invert elevation of points of connection to existing

**Figure 14–60**

17. In the *Edit Text* tab>Edit Text panel, click ☒ (Close) or click outside the text box to complete the text element.

18. Use the controls to relocate or resize the text note, if needed.

19. Zoom out to see the full sheet.

20. Save and close the project.

**End of practice**

# Practice 14e
# Add Annotations - Mechanical

## Practice Objective

- Add text with two segment leaders.

1. In the practice files *Working Models>Mechanical* folder, open **Mech-Annotate.rvt**.
2. Open the Mechanical>HVAC>3D Views>**Typ Classroom 3D HVAC Systems** view.
3. In the *Annotate* tab>Text panel, click **A** (Text).
4. In the Type Selector, select **Text: 3/32" Arial**.
5. In the *Modify | Place Text* tab>Leader panel, click ⌐**A** (2 Segments).
6. Select a point touching one of the supply air ducts and then two other points to define the leader. Type **Supply Air Ducts**, as shown in Figure 14–61, and click an empty space in the view to finish the text note.

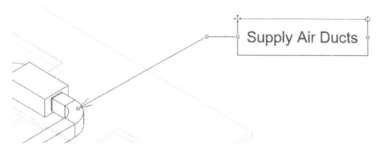

**Figure 14–61**

7. You are still in the **Text** command. Continue to add the leaders and text shown in Figure 14−62.

**Figure 14−62**

8. Save and close the project.

**End of practice**

# Practice 14f
# Add Annotations - Electrical

## Practice Objectives

- Add detail lines.
- Duplicate a text style and add text.

In this practice, you will create an area within the electrical room and add text to denote that the area needs to stay clear.

1. In the practice files *Working Models>Electrical* folder, open **Elec-Annotate.rvt**.
2. Open the Electrical>Power>Floor Plans>**01 Electrical Room** view.
3. In the *Annotate* tab>Detail panel, click 🔲 (Detail Line).
4. In the *Modify | Place Detail Lines* tab>Line Style panel, set the *Line Style* to **MEP Hidden**.
5. Draw a rectangle from the upper-left corner of the room to the lower-right corner of the room, approximately **15' x 7'-4"**, as shown in Figure 14–63.

**Figure 14–63**

6. In the *Annotate* tab>Text panel, click **A** (Text).

7. In the Type Selector, select **Text: 3/32" Arial**.

8. In Properties, click **Edit Type**. In the Type Properties dialog box, click **Duplicate**. Type **3/64" Arial - Red** for the name and click **OK**.

9. Set the following properties:

   - *Color*: **Red**
   - *Text Font*: **Arial**
   - *Text Size*: **3/64"**
   - Select **Italic**

10. Click **OK** to save and close the Type Properties dialog box.

11. Using the **3/64" Arial - Red** text type, add the following text inside the rectangular detail lines without a leader: **Keep this area clear for access to Electrical Panels**, as shown in Figure 14–64.

**Add text**

Keep this area clear
for access to
Electrical Panels

Я1-1

**Figure 14–64**

12. Save and close the project.

**End of practice**

# Practice 14g
# Add Annotations - Plumbing

## Practice Objective

- Add text with two segment leaders.

In this practice, you will annotate plumbing systems in a 3D view.

1. In the practice files *Working Models>Plumbing* folder, open **Plumb-Annotate.rvt**.

2. Open the Mechanical>Plumbing>3D Views>**Typ Classroom 3D Plumb Systems** view.

3. In the *Annotate* tab>Text panel, click **A** (Text).

4. In the Type Selector, select **Text: 3/32" Arial**.

5. In the *Modify | Place Text* tab>Leader panel, click **A** (2 Segments).

6. Select a point touching one of the hot water lines and then two other points to define the leader. Type **Domestic Hot Water**, as shown in Figure 14−65, and click in an empty space in the view to finish the text note.

**Figure 14−65**

7. You are still in the **Text** command. Add the leaders and text shown in Figure 14–66.

Domestic Hot Water ⎯

Domestic Cold Water ⎯

Sanitary ⎯

**Figure 14–66**

8. Save and close the project.

**End of practice**

# 14.3 Creating Legends

A legend is a separate view that can be placed on multiple sheets. Legends can be used to hold installation notes that need to be placed on a sheet with each floor plan, key plans, or any 2D items that need to be repeated. You can also create and list the annotations, line styles, and symbols that are used in your project, and provide explanatory notes next to the symbol, as shown in Figure 14–67. Additionally, legends can provide a list of materials or elevations of equipment used in the project.

> *Note: The elements in this figure are inserted using the **Symbol** command rather that the **Legend Component** or **Detail Component** commands.*

| Electrical Legend | |
|---|---|
| 🔒 | Dimmer Switch |
| 🔒 | 3-Way Switch |
| 🔒 | Key Operated Switch |
| ⊐ | Manual Pull Fire Alarm |

**Figure 14–67**

- You use 🔲 (Detail Line) and **A** (Text) to create the table and explanatory notes. Once you have a legend view, you can use commands, such as (Legend Component), (Detail Component), and ✚ (Symbol), to place elements in the view.

- Unlike other views, legend views can be attached to more than one sheet.

- You can set a legend's scale in the View Control Bar.

- Elements in legends can be dimensioned.

## How To: Create a Legend

1. In the *View* tab>Create panel, expand (Legends) and click (Legend), or in the Project Browser, right-click on the *Legends* area title and select **Legend**.

2. In the New Legend View dialog box, enter a name and select a scale for the legend, as shown in Figure 14–68, then click **OK**.

**Figure 14–68**

3. Place the components in the view first, and then sketch the outline of the table when you know the sizes. Use the **Reference Plane** command to line up the components.

## How To: Use Legend Components

1. In a legend view, in the *Annotate* tab>Detail panel, expand ▨ (Detail Component) and click ▨ (Legend Component).

2. In the Options Bar, select the *Family* type that you want to use, as shown in Figure 14–69.

   • This list contains all of the elements in the project that can be used in a legend. For example, you might want to display the elevation of all door types used in the project.

**Figure 14–69**

3. Select the *View* of the element that you want to place. For example, you might want to display the section or elevation of an electrical, plumbing, or mechanical fixture or equipment.

4. For section elements (such as walls, floors, and roofs), type a distance for the *Host Length*.

• Elements that are full size, such as planting components or doors, come in at their full size.

• Legends are views that can be placed on multiple sheets. You can use **Copy to the Clipboard** and **Paste** to copy legends from sheet to sheet.

# Practice 14h
# Create a Key Plan - All Disciplines

## Practice Objective

- Create a key plan, then place it on a sheet.

In this practice, you will create a key plan of the building and add it to the cover sheet.

1.  In the practice files *Working Models>General* folder, open **Gen-Key-Plan.rvt**.

2.  In the *View* tab>Create panel, expand (Legends) and click (Legend) to create a new legend view.

3.  In the New Legend View dialog box, change the *Name* to **Key Plan** and verify the *Scale* is set to **1"=100'-0"**, then click **OK**.

4.  Open the Coordination>All>Floor Plans>**Site** view.

5.  In the *Annotate* tab>Detail panel, click (Detail Line). In the Line Style panel, select **Outline**.

6.  In the Draw panel, click (Line).

7.  In the Options Bar, select **Chain**.

8.  Trace over the outer edges of the building, following the outline shown in Figure 14–70. It does not have to be exactly on the edges of the building.

    *Note: Click (Thin Lines) so the line width displays.*

Figure 14–70

9. Click  (Modify).

10. Select all of the new detail lines.

11. In the *Modify | Lines* tab>Clipboard panel, click ✂ (Cut to Clipboard).

12. Return to the Key Plan view and press <Ctrl>+<V> to paste from the clipboard. Click to place the elements and then in the *Modify | Detail Groups* tab>Edit Pasted panel, click ✓ (Finish).

13. Select all of the lines (they will be very thick if Thin Lines is not on). In the *Modify | Lines* panel>Line Style panel, change the *Line Style* to **Wide Lines**.

14. Use the modify tools to clean up the edges and add text, as shown in Figure 14–71.

# Key Plan

North Wing

South Wing

Cafeteria

Gym

Library

**Figure 14–71**

15. In the *Annotate* tab>Symbol panel, click ⊞ (Symbol).

16. In the Type Selector search path, start typing **North**. Select **North Arrow 2** and place it near the word Key Plan.

17. Drag and drop the Key Plan legend to sheet **CS-000 - Cover Sheet and place it** next to the school image.

**18.** With the legend still selected, in the Type Selector, select **Viewport: No Title** so there is no title below the key plan, as shown in Figure 14–72.

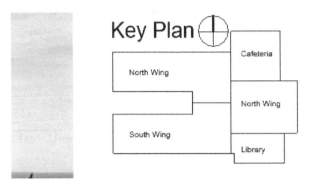

**Figure 14–72**

**19.** Zoom out to display the full sheet.

**20.** Save and close the project.

**End of practice**

# Practice 14i
# Create a Legend - Mechanical

## Practice Objectives

- Create a legend using legend components and text.
- Add the legend to a sheet.

In this practice, you will create a legend using legend components, text, and detail lines, then add it to the cover sheet.

## Task 1: Add a mechanical legend.

1.  In the practice files *Working Models>Mechanical* folder, open **Mech-Legend.rvt**.

2.  In the *View* tab>Create panel, expand ▦ (Legends) and click ▦ (Legend) to create a new legend view.

3.  Name the legend **Mechanical Legend**, set the *Scale* to **1/4"=1'-0"**, and click **OK**.

4.  In the *Annotate* tab>Detail panel, expand ◰ (Component) and click ▦ (Legend Component).

5.  In the Options Bar, add the following symbols from the *Family* list with the following views:

| Family | View |
|---|---|
| Air Terminals: Return Diffuser - Hosted: Workplane-based Return Diffuser | • Floor Plan<br>• Elevation: Front |
| Air Terminals: Supply Diffuser - Perforated - Round Neck - Ceiling Mounted: 24x24x10 In Neck | • Floor Plan<br>• Elevation: Front |
| Air Terminals: Supply Diffuser - Sidewall: 24 x 12 | • Floor Plan<br>• Elevation: Front |

**6.** Remove the front elevation details and add lines, text, and a title, as shown in Figure 14−73.

**Figure 14−73**

## Task 2: Add legend to cover sheet.

**1.** Open the **M-101- 01 Mechanical Plan** sheet.

**2.** Drag and drop the mechanical legend onto the sheet.

**3.** With the legend still selected, in the Type Selector, select **Viewport: No Title**.

**4.** Save and close the project.

**End of practice**

## Practice 14j
# Create a Legend - Electrical

### Practice Objectives

- Create a legend using legend components and text.
- Add the legend to a sheet.

In this practice, you will create a legend using legend components, text, and detail lines, then add it to the cover sheet.

### Task 1: Add an electrical legend.

1. In the practice files *Working Models>Electrical* folder, open **Elec-Legend.rvt**.

2. In the *View* tab>Create panel, expand ▦ (Legends) and click ▦ (Legend) to create a new legend view.

3. Name the legend **Light Fixtures Legend**, set the *Scale* to **1/4"=1'-0"**, and click **OK**.

4. In the *Annotate* tab>Detail panel, expand ▱ (Component) and click ▦ (Legend Component).

5. In the Options Bar, set the *View* to **Floor Plan** and *Host Length* to **0'-3"**, and place the following from the *Family* list:

   - **Lighting Fixtures : Emergency Recessed Lighting Fixture : 2x4 - 277**
   - **Lighting Fixtures : Plain Recessed Lighting Fixture : 2x4 - 277**
   - **Lighting Fixtures : Troffer Light - 2x4 Parabolic : 2'x4' (2 Lamp) - 277V**

6. Add the lines and text. Figure 14−74 shows an example of a lighting fixture legend.

**Figure 14−74**

## Task 2: Add legend to cover sheet.

1. Open the **E-101- 01 Lighting Plan sheet**.

2. With the legend still selected, in the Type Selector, select **Viewport: No Title**.

3. Drag and drop the **Light Fixtures** legend onto the sheet.

4. Save and close the project.

**End of practice**

# Practice 14k
# Create a Legend - Plumbing

## Practice Objectives

- Create a legend using legend components and text.
- Add the legend to a sheet.

In this practice, you will create a legend using legend components, text, and detail lines, then add it to the cover sheet.

## Task 1: Add a plumbing legend.

1. In the practice files *Working Models>Plumbing* folder, open **Plumb-Legend.rvt**.

2. In the *View* tab>Create panel, expand ▦ (Legends) and click ▦ (Legend) to create a new legend view.

3. Name the legend **Plumbing Fixture - Flush Tank** and set the *Scale* to **1/4"=1'-0"**, then click **OK**.

4. In the *Annotate* tab>Detail panel, expand ▱ (Component) and click ▦ (Legend Component).

5. In the Options Bar, set *Family* to **Plumbing Fixtures: Water Closet - Flush Tank: Public - 1.6 gpf** and set *View* to **Elevation - Front**. Add a single instance to the current legend view.

6. In the Options Bar, set *Family* to **Plumbing Fixtures: Water Closet - Quiet Flush Tank: Public - 1.6 gpf** and set *View* to **Elevation - Front**. Add a single instance next to the first one, as shown in Figure 14-75. Click ⌕ (Modify) to finish.

Figure 14-75

7. In the *Annotate* tab>Text panel, click **A** (Text) and label the elements, as shown in Figure 14–76.

8. Click ▯ (Detail Line) in the *Annotate* tab>Detail panel. Use the tools on the *Modify | Place Detail Lines* tab>Draw panel to add the boxes around the elements and text, as shown in Figure 14–76.

**Figure 14–76**

## Task 2:  Add legend to cover sheet.

1. Open the **P-101- 01 Plumbing Plan** sheet.

2. Drag and drop the plumbing fixture legend onto the sheet.

3. With the legend still selected, in the Type Selector, select **Viewport: No Title**.

4. Save and close the project.

**End of practice**

# Chapter Review Questions

1. When a fixture is moved, how do you update the dimension?

   a. Edit the dimension and move it over.

   b. Select the dimension and then click **Update** in the Options Bar.

   c. The dimension automatically updates.

   d. Delete the existing dimension and add a new one.

2. How do you create new text styles?

   a. Using the **Text Styles** command.

   b. Duplicate an existing type.

   c. They must be included in a template.

   d. Using the **Format Styles** command.

3. When you edit text, how many leaders can be added using the leader tools shown in Figure 14–77?

**Figure 14–77**

   a. One

   b. One on each end of the text

   c. As many as you want at each end of the text

4. Detail lines created in one view also display in the related view.

   a. True

   b. False

5. Which of the following describes the difference between a symbol and a component?

   a. Symbols are 3D and only display in one view. Components are 2D and display in many views.

   b. Symbols are 2D and only display in one view. Components are 3D and display in many views.

   c. Symbols are 2D and display in many views. Components are 3D and only display in one view.

   d. Symbols are 3D and display in many views. Components are 2D and only display in one view.

6. When creating a legend, which of the following elements cannot be added?

   a. Legend components

   b. Tags

   c. Rooms

   d. Symbols

# Command Summary

| Button | Command | Location |
|---|---|---|
| **Dimensions and Text** | | |
| | **Aligned (Dimension)** | • **Ribbon:** *Annotate* tab>Dimension panel or *Modify* tab>Measure panel, expanded drop-down list<br>• **Quick Access Toolbar**<br>• **Shortcut:** DI |
| | **Angular (Dimension)** | • **Ribbon:** *Annotate* tab>Dimension panel or *Modify* tab>Measure panel, expanded drop-down list |
| | **Arc Length (Dimension)** | • **Ribbon:** *Annotate* tab>Dimension panel or *Modify* tab>Measure panel, expanded drop-down list |
| | **Diameter (Dimension)** | • **Ribbon:** *Annotate* tab>Dimension panel or *Modify* tab>Measure panel, expanded drop-down list |
| | **Linear (Dimension)** | • **Ribbon:** *Annotate* tab>Dimension panel or *Modify* tab>Measure panel, expanded drop-down list |
| | **Radial (Dimension)** | • **Ribbon:** *Annotate* tab>Dimension panel or *Modify* tab>Measure panel, expanded drop-down list |
| **A** | **Text** | • **Ribbon:** *Annotate* tab>Text panel<br>• **Shortcut:** TX |
| **Detail Lines and Symbols** | | |
| | **Detail Line** | • **Ribbon:** *Annotate* tab>Detail panel<br>• **Shortcut:** DL |
| | **Stair Path** | • **Ribbon:** *Annotate* tab>Symbol panel |
| | **Symbol** | • **Ribbon:** *Annotate* tab>Symbol panel |
| **Legends** | | |
| | **Legend (View)** | • **Ribbon:** *View* tab>Create panel, expand Legends |
| | **Legend Component** | • **Ribbon:** *Annotate* tab>Detail panel, expand Component |

# Adding Tags and Schedules

Adding tags to your views helps you to identify elements such as doors, windows, or walls in the model. Tags are 2D annotation families with labels that extract information about the elements being tagged from their properties. Tags are typically added when you insert an element, but can also be added at any point in the design process. The information captured in the elements in a project is used to populate schedules, which can be added to sheets to complete the construction documents.

## Learning Objectives

- Add tags to elements in 2D and 3D views to prepare the views to be placed on sheets.
- Load tags that are required for projects.
- Modify schedule content, including the instance and type properties of related elements.
- Add schedules to sheets as part of the construction documents.

# 15.1 Adding Tags

Tags identify elements that are listed in schedules. Door and window tags are inserted automatically if you use the **Tag on Placement** option when inserting the door or window or other elements. You can also add them later to specific views as needed. Many other types of tags are available in Revit, such as air terminal, duct, mechanical equipment and piping tags, as shown in Figure 15–1.

*Note: Additional tags are stored in the Revit Library in the Annotations folder.*

**Figure 15–1**

- The **Tag by Category** command works for most elements, except for a few that have separate commands.

- Tags can be letters, numbers, or a combination of the two.

You can place three types of tags, as follows:

- (Tag by Category): Tags according to the category of the element. It places door tags on doors and wall tags on walls.

- (Multi-Category Tag): Tags elements belonging to multiple categories. The tags display information from parameters that they have in common.

- (Material Tag): Tags that display the type of material. They are typically used in detailing.

### How To: Add Tags

1.  In the *Annotate* tab>Tag panel, click 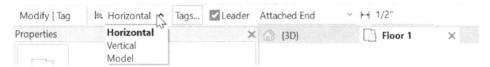 (Tag by Category), (Multi-Category Tag), or (Material Tag) depending on the type of tag you want to place.

2.  In the Options Bar, set the options as needed, as shown in Figure 15–2.

**Figure 15–2**

3.  Select the element you want to tag. If a tag for the selected element is not loaded, you are prompted to load it from the Revit Library.

## Tag Options

*   In the Options Bar, you can set tag options for leaders and tag orientation, as shown in Figure 15–3. You can also press <Spacebar> to toggle the rotation while placing or modifying the tag.

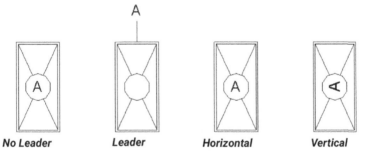

No Leader     Leader     Horizontal     Vertical

**Figure 15–3**

*   Tag orientation can be set to the following:

    *   **Horizontal:** Tag stays horizontal (0°) to the element it is tagging.

    *   **Vertical:** Forces the tag to stay vertical (90°) to the element it is tagging no matter what.

    *   **Model:** Tag rotates freely from the element, similar to room tags.

- Leaders can have an **Attached End** or a **Free End**, as shown in Figure 15−4. The attached end must be connected to the element being tagged. A free end has an additional drag control where the leader touches the element.

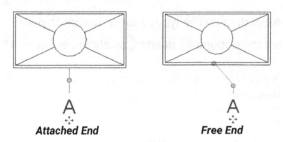

Attached End           Free End

Figure 15−4

- If you change between **Attached End** and **Free End**, the tag does not move and the leader does not change location.

- The **Length** option specifies the length of the leader in plotting units. It is grayed out if **Leader** is not selected or if a **Free End** leader is defined.

- If a tag is not loaded, a No Tag Loaded dialog box opens, as shown in Figure 15−5. Click **Yes** to open the Load Family dialog box in which you can select the appropriate tag.

Figure 15−5

- Tags can be pinned so they stay in place if you move the element that is tagged. This is primarily used when tags have leaders, as shown in Figure 15−6.

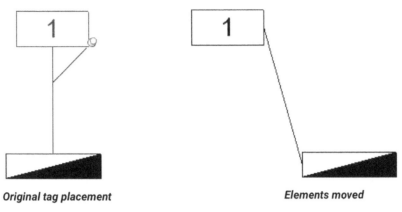

*Original tag placement*                    *Elements moved*

**Figure 15−6**

## Multi-Leader Tags

If you have elements that need to be tagged that are in close proximity to one another, you can tag one element and then select other similar elements. This adds more leader lines from the elements to the tag, as shown with the electrical outlets in Figure 15−7. When selecting the tag, you can see how many host elements it is tagging in Properties (as shown on the left in Figure 15−7).

You cannot select elements that are of different categories, like air handling units (AHUs) and panels. You can only select similar elements to share a tag.

**Figure 15−7**

If you select, for instance, two air terminal types that are different sizes, you will get a <varies> tag, as shown in Figure 15−8, because they are not the same size.

**Figure 15−8**

You can modify how the leaders are displayed when using the multi-leader tags. You can adjust how they will display in the view by showing all leaders, hiding select leaders, or hiding all leaders.

| | |
|---|---|
| (Show All Leaders) | This turns on all leaders of any tag that is selected that used Multi-Leader tagging. |
| (Hide All Leaders) | This turns off all leaders of any tag that is selected that used Multi-Leader tagging. |
| (Show One Leader) | This turns off all leaders except for one leader of any tag that is selected that used Multi-Leader tagging. |
| (Select Leaders to Show) | This puts you into edit mode and enables you to select specific leaders to show or hide. When finished, you need to click ✅ (Finish). |
| (Merge Leaders) | Select to turn this feature on. This will merge all the leader line elbows to one location on the main leader line. You will not have the ability to adjust the leader lines individually. To get the leader line elbows back, select the **Merge Leaders** icon. |

## How To: Add a Multi-Leader Tag

1.  Start the **Tag by Category** command.

2.  Set the Options Bar settings.

3.  Tag one element in the model.

4.  Verify **Add/Remove Host** is on, as shown in Figure 15–9.

**Figure 15–9**

5.  Select the other similar elements to add to the tag.

•   Alternatively, if you have a tag already placed in the model and you want to add elements to

    the tag, select the tag, and in the contextual tab, click ⚒ (Add/Remove Host), then select
    the other elements.

6.  Set the leaders options as needed.

7.  A leader line will be added for each element you select.

## How To: Remove Elements from a Multi-Leader Tag

1.  To remove an element from the tag, select the tag and in the ribbon, select ⚒ (Add/
    Remove Host).

2.  Select the element in the model. The leader line is removed.

## How To: Add Multiple Tags

1. In the *Annotate* tab>Tag panel, click  (Tag All).

2. In the Tag All Not Tagged dialog box (shown in Figure 15–10), select the checkbox beside one or more categories to tag. Selecting the checkbox beside the *Category* title selects all of the tags.

   *Note: To tag only some elements, select them before starting this command. In the Tag All Not Tagged dialog box, select **Only selected objects in current view**.*

**Click to select all tags in the list** ——▶

Figure 15–10

3. Set the *Leader* and *Tag Orientation* as needed.

4. Click **Apply** to apply the tags and stay in the dialog box. Click **OK** to apply the tags and close the dialog box.

- When you select a tag, the properties of that tag display. To display the properties of the tagged element, in the *Modify* contextual tab>Host panel, click (Select Host).

## How To: Load Tags

1. In the *Annotate* tab, expand the Tag panel and click  (Loaded Tags And Symbols) or, when a Tag command is active, in the Options Bar, click **Tags...**.

2. In the Loaded Tags And Symbols dialog box (shown in Figure 15–11), click **Load Family...**.

**Figure 15–11**

3. In the Load Family dialog box, navigate to the appropriate *Annotations* folder in the Revit Library, select the tag(s) needed, and click **Open**.

4. The tag is added to the category in the dialog box. Click **OK**.

## Instance vs. Type Based Tags

Many elements (such as air terminals) are tagged in a numbered sequence, with each instance of the air terminal having a separate tag number. Other elements (such as lighting and plumbing fixtures) are tagged by type, as shown in Figure 15–12. Changing the information in one tag changes all instances of that element.

Figure 15–12

- To modify the number of an instance tag (such as a light fixture or air terminal), slowly click twice directly on the number in the tag and modify it, or you can modify the *Mark* property, as shown in Figure 15–13. Only that one instance updates.

Figure 15–13

- To modify the number of a type tag, you can slowly click twice directly on the number in the tag and modify it. Alternatively, you can select the element and in Properties, click  (Edit Type). In the Type Properties dialog box, in the *Identity Data* section, modify the *Type Mark*, as shown in Figure 15–14. All instances of this element then update.

**Figure 15–14**

- When you change a type tag, an alert box opens to warn you that changing a type parameter affects other elements, as shown in Figure 15–15. If you want this tag to modify all other elements of this type, click **Yes**.

**Figure 15–15**

- If a tag displays with a question mark, it means that no information has been assigned to that element's parameter yet.

# Tagging in 3D Views

You can add tags to isometric 3D views, as shown in Figure 15–16, as long as the views are locked first. Locking a 3D view enables you to create the view as you want it and then save it from being modified.

**Figure 15–16**

- You must lock an isometric 3D view in order to place tags. Dimensions can be added to isometric 3D views whether they are locked or not. Proceed with caution when selecting the items to dimension to ensure that the witness lines and text orient is snapping to and extending in the correct direction as intended.You cannot tag or add dimensions in a perspective view, as these are views created with the camera tool.

## How To: Lock a 3D View

1. Open a 3D view and set it up as you want it to display.

   *Note: When adding text in a 3D view, you do not have to lock the view. When tagging in a 3D view, you have to lock the view.*

2. In the View Control Bar, click 🏠 (Unlocked 3D View), then click 🏠 (Save Orientation and Lock View).

- If you are using the default 3D view and it has not been saved, you are prompted to name and save the view first.

- You can modify the orientation of the view by clicking 🏠 (Locked 3D View), then clicking 🏠 (Unlock View). This also removes any tags you have applied.

- To return to the previous locked view, click 🏠 (Unlocked 3D View), then click 🏠 (Restore Orientation and Lock View).

# Practice 15a
# Add Tags - Mechanical

## Practice Objectives

- Use the Tag All Not Tagged dialog box.
- Modify tags.
- Modify tags using the **Add/Remove Host** tool.

In this practice, you will use the **Tag All** tool to add duct, pipe, and air terminal tags to a mechanical floor plan, then you will modify the tags and use the **Add/Remove Host** tool to combined similar tags to reduce confusion.

## Task 1:  Tag all not tagged.

1. In the practice files *Working Models>Mechanical* folder, open **Mech-Tags.rvt**.

2. Open the Mechanical>HVAC>Floor Plans**>01 Mechanical - North Wing** view. There are tags on the ducting and the air terminals.

3. Open the **01 Mechanical - South Wing** view. This view is missing its tags. (Type **ZF** or **ZA** to fit the model in the view if it is not showing.)

4. In the *Annotate* tab>Tag panel, click ⌂ (Tag All).

5. In the Tag All Not Tagged dialog box, select the following:

   - *Air Terminal Tags:* **Diffuser Tag**
   - *Mechanical Equipment Tags:* **ASCENT: ME Combination Tag**

6. Verify that the **Leader** is unchecked and click **OK**.

   - If a warning dialog box displays about Elements Have Hidden Tags, click **OK**.

7. All of the air terminals and mechanical equipment are now tagged in this view, as shown in part in Figure 15–17.

**Figure 15–17**

8. Save the project.

## Task 2: Modify tags.

1. Zoom in to the upper-left classroomsin the south wing (next to the stairwell) and move the air diffuser tags so they are not on top of any other element and are closer to the diffusers. Select the AHU mechanical equipment tag on the mechanical equipment that is the farthest one to the left in the south wing hallway.

2. In the *Modify | Edit Tags* tab>Host panel, select ⚒ (Add/Remove Host). In the Options Bar, check the checkbox next to **Leader**.

3. Select the AHU (not the tag) on the other side of the hallway, as shown in Figure 15–18.

**Figure 15–18**

4. Click ⛶ (Modify).

*Note: While selecting leader from the Options Bar, you can also change the orientation from Horizontal to Vertical if required.*

5.  Select the left AHU tag and drag it away from the AHU unit, as shown in Figure 15–19. You will see leaders pointing to both ducts.

**Figure 15–19**

6.  Click  (Modify).

7.  You can delete the unneeded AHU tag.

8.  Repeat the process for any AHU tags that are close to each other.

9.  Save and close the project.

**End of practice**

# Practice 15b
# Add Tags - Electrical

## Practice Objectives

- Add tags to a model.
- Use the Tag All Not Tagged dialog box.
- Set the Type Mark parameter for tags.
- Modify tags using the **Add/Remove Host** tool.

In this practice, you will add light fixture tags and conduit tags to electrical floor plans and modify the elements' type marks. You will then modify the tags and use the **Add/Remove Host** tool to combine similar tags to reduce confusion.

## Task 1: Add tags to a lighting floor plan.

1. In the practice files *Working Models>Electrical* folder, open **Elec-Tags.rvt**.

2. Open the Electrical>Lighting>Floor Plans>**01 Lighting Plan - North Wing** view. There are tags on the light fixtures displaying different ways to use tags.

3. Open the **01 Lighting - South Wing** view. This view is missing its tags. (Type **ZF** or **ZA** to fit the model in the view if it is not showing.)

4. In the *Annotate* tab>Tag panel, click 🏷️ (Tag All).

5. In the Tag All Not Tagged dialog box, do the following:

   - Select **Lighting Fixture Tags**.
   - Verify the *Loaded Tags* column is set to **Lighting Fixture Tag: Standard**.
   - Select **Leader**.
   - Verify the *Leader Length* is **1/16"**.
   - Verify the *Tag Orientation* is **Horizontal**.

6.  Click **OK**. The lights that were not tagged are now tagged, as shown in Figure 15–20. The emergency light fixture tags have a question mark. This means they do not have a type mark assigned to them.

**Figure 15–20**

7.  Click 🖱 (Modify) and select the emergency recessed light fixture. In Properties, click 🗔 (Edit Type).

8.  In the Type Properties dialog box, in the *Identity Data* area, set the *Type Mark* to **E1** and click **OK**. All of the emergency light fixture tags update to display this information, as shown in two of the classrooms in Figure 15–21.

**Figure 15–21**

9.  In the *Annotate* tab>Tag panel, click 🔖 (Tag by Category).

10. In the Options Bar, verify that **Horizontal**, **Leader**, and **Attached End** are selected and that the *Leader Length* is set to **1/16"**.

11. Click the **Tags...** button.

12. In the Loaded Tags And Symbols dialog box, verify that *Lighting Fixtures* shows the default **Lighting Fixture Tag: Standard** tag in the *Loaded Tags* column, as shown in Figure 15–22.

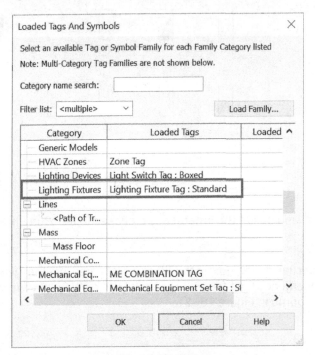

**Figure 15–22**

13. In the top leftmost classroom in the **01 Lighting - South Wing** view, tag the light fixtures at the bottom, as shown in Figure 15–23. It should appear that you have duplicate tags for each light fixture. Do not tag any other classrooms at this time.

**Figure 15–23**

14. Click  (Modify) and select all the tags below the lights.

15. In the Type Selector, select **Lighting Fixture Circuit Tag: Standard**. The tag information changes from displaying the light fixture number to the circuit number, as shown in Figure 15–24.

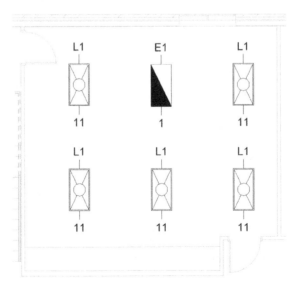

**Figure 15–24**

• Note that the tags could be combined using the **Add/Remove Host** tool.

**16.** Select the lower left light fixture circuit **11** tag. In the *Modify | Lighting Fixture Tags* tab>Host panel, select 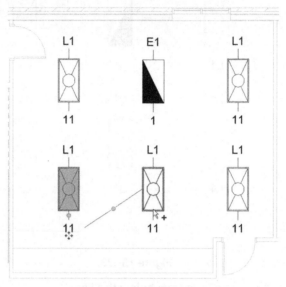 (Add/Remove Host).

**17.** Select the light fixture to the right, as shown in Figure 15–25.

**Figure 15–25**

**18.** Select the rest of the light fixtures in the classroom, including the E1 light fixture. Because the light fixture E1 is not on the same circuit, your tag will display **<varies>**, as shown in Figure 15–26. Select the E1 light fixture to remove it from the selection, and the tag will return to 11.

**Figure 15–26**

**19.** Click ⬚ (Modify).

**20.** Drag the tag to the center of the classroom and delete the unneeded circuit tags, as shown in Figure 15–27. You will see leaders pointing to the light fixtures. Adjust the leaders using the grips as needed so other tags can be seen as well.

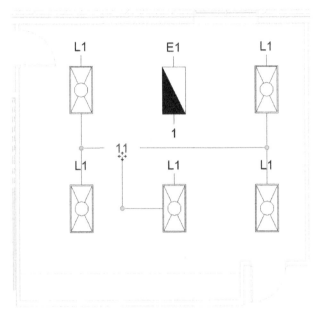

**Figure 15–27**

**21.** Click ⬚ (Modify).

**22.** Continue tagging the rest of the classrooms, changing the tag type and merging tags using the **Add/Remove Host** tool.

**23.** Save the project.

## Task 2:  Load and use a conduit tag.

**1.** Open the Electrical>Power>Floor Plans>**01 Power Plan** view.

**2.** Zoom in on the same rooms you worked in with the light fixtures.

**3.** In the *Annotate* tab>Tag panel, click ⬚ (Tag All).

**4.** In the Tag All Not Tagged dialog box, do the following:

- Select **Conduit Tag**.

- Deselect **Leader**, if applicable.

- Set the *Tag Orientation* to **Horizontal**.

5. Click **OK**. The conduits are now tagged, as shown in Figure 15–28.

**Figure 15–28**

6. Click ⟍ (Modify) and select the conduit in the smaller classroom.

7. In the Options Bar, change the *Diameter* to **3/4"**. The tag updates automatically, as shown in Figure 15–29.

**Figure 15–29**

8. Type **ZF** to zoom out to fit the view.

9. Save and close the project.

**End of practice**

# Practice 15c
# Add Tags - Plumbing

## Practice Objectives

- Add tags to a model.
- Lock a 3D view to tag plumbing systems and fixtures.
- Modify the Type Mark parameter for tags.

In this practice, you will add plumbing fixture tags and rotate a 3D view and lock it into place. You will then add tags to plumbing systems and fixtures, then modify the fixtures' type mark to update the tags.

## Task 1: Add tags to a floor plan.

1. In the practice files *Working Models>Plumbing* folder, open **Plumb-Tags.rvt**.
2. Duplicate the **3D Plumbing** view and rename it to **3D Plumbing - 2nd Floor Restroom**.
3. Select the linked architectural model and type **VH** to hide it in the view.

   *Note: Alternatively, you can select the restroom items and from the Modify | Multi-Select*

   *tab, select* 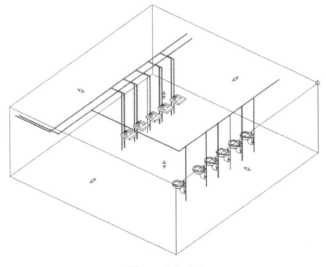 *Section Box.*

4. In Properties, turn on **Section Box** and use the control grips to only see the second floor bathroom, as shown in Figure 15–30.

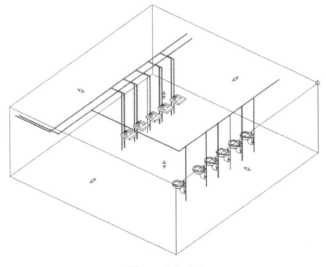

**Figure 15–30**

5.  With the section box still selected, right-click and select **Hide in View>Elements** to hide the section box.

6.  In the View Control Bar, click 🏠 (Unlocked 3D View) and select **Save Orientation and Lock View** to lock the view in place.

7.  In the *Annotate* tab>Tag panel, click ⬡① (Tag by Category). In the Options Bar, set the tag orientation to **Horizontal** and uncheck **Leader**. Tag the pipe.

8.  While still in the **Tag by Category** command, do the following in the Options Bar:

    •   Check **Leader**.

    •   Check **Attached End**.

    •   Set the *Leader Length* to **1/8"**.

9.  Tag one lavatory and one water closet.

10. Click ▹ (Modify).

11. The new tags appear empty but when you select them, they both have question marks for their tags.

12. Click ▹ (Modify).

13. Save the project.

## Task 2: Modify plumbing fixtures to update the tags.

1.  Select one of the lavatories. In Properties, click ▤ (Edit Type).

2.  In the Type Properties dialog box, in the *Identity Data* area, set the *Type Mark* to **LS2** and click **OK**. The tags update in the view.

3.  Repeat the process with a water closet and set the *Type Mark* to **WC2**.

4.  In the *Annotate* tab>Tag panel, click ⬡ (Tag All).

5.  In the Tag All Not Tagged dialog box, do the following:

    •   Check **Plumbing Fixture Tags** and verify the *Loaded Tags* column is set to **Tags Plumbing Fixture Tag : Boxed**.

    •   Check **Leader**.

    •   Set the *Leader Length* to **1/8"**.

    •   Set the *Tag Orientation* to **Horizontal**.

6.  Click **OK**. The lavatories and water closets are now tagged.

    •   The tags for all the lavatories and water closets will be the same because the tag is pulling parameter information from the elements' type properties.

7.  Select the first water closet tag. In the *Modify | Duct Tags* tab>Host panel, select ⬡ (Add/ Remove Host).

8.  Select the other water closets. Drag the tag out from the water closets, as shown in Figure 15–31. Delete the unneeded tags.

**Figure 15–31**

9.  Click ⬉ (Modify).

10. Repeat **Add/Remove Host** for the lavatory tags.

11. Adjust the view scale if needed.

12. Save and close the project.

**End of practice**

# 15.2 Working with Schedules

Schedules extract information from a project and display it in table form. Each schedule is stored as a separate view and can be placed on sheets, as shown in Figure 15–32. Any changes you make to the project elements that affect the schedules are automatically updated in both views and sheets.

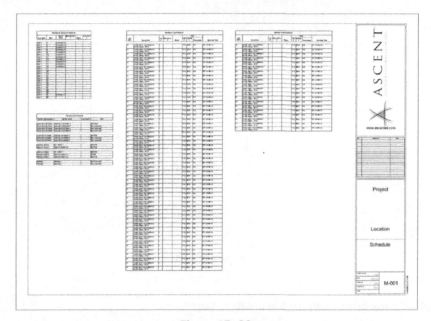

Figure 15–32

- The default MEP templates do not include any schedules; however, the **Construction-Default.rte**, **Residential-Default.rte**, and **Commercial-Default.rte** template files include useful schedules.

## Work with Schedules

- In the Project Browser, expand the **Schedules/Quantities** node, as shown in Figure 15–33, and double-click on the schedule you want to open.

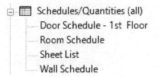

Figure 15–33

- Schedules are automatically filled out with the information stored in the instance and type parameters of related elements that are added to the model. Fill out additional information either in the schedule or in Properties.

- In the *Modify Schedule/Quantities* tab>Appearance panel, you can select ⬚ (Freeze Header) to keep the header row visible while you scroll through the schedule.

- When selecting on a schedule's row, it will highlight in blue.

- You can drag and drop the schedule onto a sheet.

- You can zoom in to read small text in schedule views. Hold down <Ctrl> and scroll using the mouse wheel or press <Ctrl>+<+> to zoom in or <Ctrl>+<-> to zoom out.

## How To: Create a Schedule

1. In the *View* tab>Create panel, expand ⬚ (Schedules) and click ⬚ (Schedule/Quantities), or in the Project Browser, right-click on the **Schedules/Quantities** node and select **New Schedule/Quantities**.

2. In the New Schedule dialog box, select the type of schedule you want to create (e.g., Doors) from the *Category* list, as shown in Figure 15–34.

   *Note: In the Filter list drop-down list, you can specify the discipline(s) to show only the categories that you want to display.*

**Figure 15–34**

3. Revit assigns a name for the schedule. You can also type a new *Name* if the default does not suit.

4. Select **Schedule building components**.

5. Specify the *Phase*, as needed.

6. Click **OK**.

7. Fill out the information in the Schedule Properties dialog box. This includes the information in the *Fields*, *Filter*, *Sorting/Grouping*, *Formatting*, and *Appearance* tabs.

8. Once you have entered the schedule properties, click **OK**. A schedule view is created, displaying a report of the information configured in the schedule.

• Other elements that can be scheduled include model groups and Revit links.

## Schedule Properties – Fields Tab

In the *Fields* tab, you can select from a list of available fields and organize them in the order in which you want them to display in the schedule, as shown in Figure 15–35. You can also sort the available fields by *Parameter Type* (such as Project Parameters), *Discipline*, or *Value Type*.

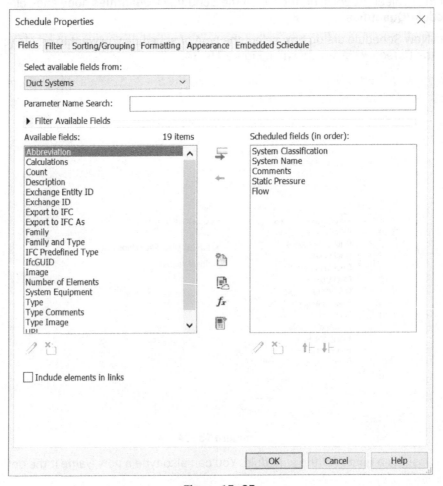

**Figure 15–35**

## How To: Fill Out the Fields Tab

1.  In the *Available fields* area, select one or more fields you want to add to the schedule and

    click ⬇ (Add parameter(s)). The field(s) are placed in the *Scheduled fields (in order)* area.
2.  Continue adding fields, as required.

    *   Click ⬅ (Remove parameter(s)) to move a field from the *Scheduled fields* area back to
        the *Available fields* area.

    *Note: You can also double-click on a field to move it from the Available fields area to the
    Scheduled fields area, and double-click on a field to remove it from the Scheduled fields
    area.*

    *   Use ↑E (Move parameter up) and ↓E (Move parameter down) to change the order of
        the scheduled fields.

## Other Fields Tab Options

| | |
|---|---|
| **Select available fields from** | Enables you to select additional category fields for the specified schedule. The available list of fields depends on the original category of the schedule. Typically, they include room information. |
| **Include elements in links** | Includes elements that are in files linked to the current project, so that their elements can be included in the schedule. |
| **(New parameter)** | Adds a new field according to your specification. New fields can be placed by instance or by type. |
| $f_x$ **(Add Calculated parameter)** | Enables you to create a field that uses a formula based on other fields. |
| **(Combine parameters)** | Enables you to combine two or more parameters in one column.You can put any fields together even if they are used in another column. |
| **(Edit parameter)** | Enables you to edit custom fields. This is grayed out if you select a standard field. |
| **(Delete parameter)** | Deletes the selected custom fields. This is grayed out if you select a standard field. |

## Schedule Properties – Filter Tab

In the *Filter* tab, you can set up filters so that only elements meeting specific criteria are included in the schedule. For example, you might only want to show information for one level, as shown in Figure 15–36. You can create filters for up to eight values. All values must be satisfied for the elements to display.

**Figure 15–36**

- The parameter you want to use as a filter must be included in the schedule. You can hide the parameter once you have completed the schedule, if needed.

| Filter by | |
|---|---|
| **Field/Parameter** | Specifies the field/parameter to filter. Not all fields/parameters are available to be used to filter. |
| **Condition** | Specifies the condition that must be met. This includes options such as **equal**, **not equal**, **greater than**, and **less than**. |
| **Value** | Specifies the value of the element to be filtered. You can select from a drop-down list of appropriate values. For example, if you set *Filter by* to **Level**, it displays the list of levels in the project. |

## Schedule Properties – Sorting/Grouping Tab

In the *Sorting/Grouping* tab, you can set how you want the information to be sorted, as shown in Figure 15–37. For example, you can sort by **Mark** (number) and then **Type**.

**Figure 15–37**

| Sort by | Enables you to select the field(s) you want to sort by. You can select up to four levels of sorting. |
|---|---|
| Ascending/ Descending | Sorts fields in **Ascending** or **Descending** order based on an alphanumeric system. |
| Header/Footer | Enables you to group similar information and separate it by a **Header** with a title and/or a **Footer** with quantity information. |
| Blank line | Adds a blank line between groups. |
| Grand totals | Selects which totals to display for the entire schedule. You can specify a name to display in the schedule for the grand total. |
| Itemize every instance | If selected, displays each instance of the element in the schedule. If not selected, displays only one instance of each type based on the sorting/ grouping categories, as shown in Figure 15–38. |

| <Duct System Schedule> | | | | |
|---|---|---|---|---|
| A | B | C | D | E |
| System Classificatio | System Name | Comments | Static Pressure | Flow |
| Return Air | <varies> | | 0.00 in-wg | 0 CFM |
| Return Air | <varies> | | 0.06 in-wg | 500 CFM |
| Return Air | 01 - RA08 | | 0.11 in-wg | 500 CFM |
| Return Air | RA 1 | | 0.15 in-wg | 1000 CFM |
| Return Air | <varies> | | 0.20 in-wg | <varies> |
| Return Air | <varies> | | 0.21 in-wg | <varies> |

**Figure 15–38**

# Schedule Properties – Formatting Tab

In the *Formatting* tab, you can control how the headers of each field display, as shown in Figure 15–39. The *Multiple values indication* options enable you to control how fields with multiple values display.

**Figure 15–39**

| Fields | Enables you to select the field for which you want to modify the formatting. |
|---|---|
| Heading | Enables you to change the heading of the field if you want it to be different from the field name. For example, you might want to replace **Mark** (a generic name) with the more specific **Door Number** in a door schedule. |

| Heading orientation | Enables you to set the heading on sheets to **Horizontal** or **Vertical**. This does not impact the schedule view. |
|---|---|
| Alignment | Aligns the text in rows under the heading to be **Left**, **Right**, or **Center** justified. |
| Field Format... | Sets the units format for numerical fields, e.g., length, area, HVAC air flow, pipe flow, etc. By default, this is set to use the project settings. |
| Conditional Format... | Sets up the schedule to display visual feedback based on the conditions listed. |
| Hidden field | Enables you to hide a field. For example, you might want to use a field for sorting purposes, but not have it display in the schedule. You can also modify this option in the schedule view later. |
| Show conditional format on sheets | Select if you want the color code set up in the Conditional Format dialog box to display on sheets. |
| Calculation options | Select the type of calculation you want to use.<br>• **No Calculation:** All values in a field are calculated separately.<br>• **Calculate totals:** All values in a field are added together. This enables a field to calculate and display in the Grand Totals or Footers.<br>• **Calculate minimum:** Only the smallest amount displays.<br>• **Calculate maximum:** Only the largest amount displays.<br>• **Calculate minimum and maximum:** Both the smallest and largest amounts display.<br>Minimum and maximum calculations only show when **Itemize every instance** is unchecked in the *Sorting/Grouping* tab. |
| Multiple values indication | When a schedule is not set to itemize every instance, select how the value will display. |

### 💡 Hint: Hiding Columns

If you want to use the field to filter or sort, but do not want it to display in the schedule, select **Hidden field**. Alternatively, once the schedule is completed, select the column header, right-click on it, and select **Hide Columns**.

# Schedule Properties – Appearance Tab

In the *Appearance* tab, you can set the text style and grid options for a schedule, as shown in Figure 15–40.

**Figure 15–40**

| | |
|---|---|
| **Grid lines** | Displays lines between each instance listed and around the outside of the schedule. Select the style of lines from the drop-down list; this controls all lines for the schedule, unless modified. |
| **Grid in headers/footers/ spacers** | Extends the vertical grid lines between the columns. |
| **Outline** | Specify a different line type for the outline of the schedule. |
| **Blank row before data** | Select this option if you want a blank row to be displayed before the data begins in the schedule. |
| **Stripe Rows** | Select this option if you want to highlight alternating rows within the schedule to help differentiate the rows in large schedules. |

| | |
|---|---|
| **Show Title/Show Headers** | Select these options to include the text in the schedule. |
| **Title text/Header text/ Body text** | Select the text style for the title, header, and body text. |

# Schedule View Properties

Schedule views have properties, including the *View Template, View Name, Phases*, and methods of returning to the Schedule Properties dialog box (as shown in Figure 15−41). In the *Other* section, click the button next to the tab name that you want to open in the Schedule Properties dialog box. In the dialog box, you can switch from tab to tab and make any required changes to the overall schedule.

**Figure 15−41**

Just like other views, schedules can have view templates applied. When you specify a view template directly in the view, none of the schedule properties can be modified, as shown in Figure 15–42.

**Figure 15–42**

- Schedule view templates are type-specific. If you apply one to a different type of element, only the *Appearance* information is applied.

- If you apply a schedule view template to a schedule of the same type, it overrides everything in the existing schedule, including the fields.

- If you have a complicated schedule, you might want to create a view template for it to avoid losing that organization.

- To create schedule view templates, you need to create at least one from an existing view, then you can modify it and duplicate it in the View Templates dialog box.

# Filtering Elements from Schedules

When you create schedules based on a category, you might need to filter out some of the element types in that category. For example, in Revit, doors (and windows) in curtain walls are automatically added to a door schedule, as shown at the top in Figure 15–43, but are typically estimated as part of the curtain wall rather than as a separate door. To remove them from the schedule, as shown at the bottom in Figure 15–43, assign a parameter that identifies them and then use that parameter to filter them out of the schedule.

**All plumbing fixtures displayed**

| <Plumbing Fixture Schedule> | | | |
|---|---|---|---|
| **A** | **B** | **C** | **D** |
| Family | Type | Count | System Name |
| Floor Drain - Round | 5" Strainer - 3" Drain | 7 | |
| Lavatory - Rectangular | 22"x22" - Public | 20 | Domestic Cold Water 1,Domestic Hot Water 1,Sanitary 1 |
| Sink - Island - Single | 30"x21" - Public | 40 | Domestic Cold Water 1,Domestic Hot Water 1,Sanitary 1 |
| Urinal - Wall Hung | 1" Flush Valve | 6 | Domestic Cold Water 1,Sanitary 1 |
| Water Closet - Flush Valve - Wall Mounted | Public - Flushing Greater than 1.6 gpf | 20 | Domestic Cold Water 1,Sanitary 1 |

**Floor drains filtered out**

| <Plumbing Fixture Schedule> | | | |
|---|---|---|---|
| **A** | **B** | **C** | **D** |
| Family | Type | Count | System Name |
| Lavatory - Rectangular | 22"x22" - Public | 20 | Domestic Cold Water 1,Domestic Hot Water 1,Sanitary 1 |
| Sink - Island - Single | 30"x21" - Public | 40 | Domestic Cold Water 1,Domestic Hot Water 1,Sanitary 1 |
| Urinal - Wall Hung | 1" Flush Valve | 6 | Domestic Cold Water 1,Sanitary 1 |
| Water Closet - Flush Valve - Wall Mounted | Public - Flushing Greater than 1.6 gpf | 20 | Domestic Cold Water 1,Sanitary 1 |

**Figure 15–43**

- This type of filtering can be used for any schedule in any discipline.

## How To: Filter Elements in a Schedule

1. Select an element (such as a sink) and modify the Type Parameters. Add a value to one of the parameters that you are not otherwise using in your schedule. For example, you could set *Type Mark* to **S01**, as shown Figure 15–44.

**Figure 15–44**

2. Create a schedule and include the field for the parameter you used (such as *Type Mark* in the above example).

3.  Modify the *Filter* of the schedule so that the parameter equals the specified value. In the example shown in Figure 15–45, the filter is set so **Type Mark** > **equals** > **S01**. Any types that match this filter are included in the schedule.

**Figure 15–45**

4.  In the final schedule, the elements display with the specified value. Right-click on the column header for the parameter you used to filter the schedule and select **Hide Columns**, as shown in Figure 15–46. It is just used as a filter and does not need to be part of the final schedule.

*Note: Hiding a parameter/field in a schedule enables you to use it as a filter, but not have it visible in the schedule.*

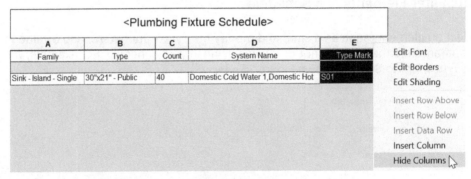

**Figure 15–46**

# Modifying Schedules

Information in schedules is bi-directional:

- Make changes to elements and the schedule automatically updates.

- Make changes to information in the schedule cells and the elements automatically update.

### How To: Modify Schedule Cells

1. Open the schedule view.

2. Select the cell you want to change. Some cells have drop-down lists, as shown in Figure 15–47. Others have edit fields.

Figure 15–47

3. Add the new information. The change is reflected in the schedule, on the sheet, and in the elements of the project.

- If you change a type property, an alert box opens, as shown in Figure 15–48.

Figure 15–48

*Note: If you change a type property in the schedule, it applies to all elements of that type. If you change an instance property, it only applies to that one element.*

- When you select an element in a schedule, in the *Modify Schedule/Quantities* tab>Element panel, you can click ![icon] (Highlight in Model). This opens a close-up view of the element with the Show Element(s) in View dialog box, as shown in Figure 15–49. Click **Show** to display more views of the element. Click **Close** to finish the command.

**Figure 15–49**

### 💡 Hint: Customizing Schedules

Schedules are typically included in project templates, which are set up by the BIM manager or other advanced users. They can be complex to create as there are many options.

- For information on using schedule data outside of Revit, see *B.5 Importing and Exporting Schedules*.

- For more information about creating schedules, refer to the ASCENT guide *Autodesk Revit: BIM Management: Template and Family Creation*.

# Modifying a Schedule on a Sheet

Once you have placed a schedule on a sheet, you can manipulate it to fit the information into the available space. Select the schedule to display the controls that enable you to modify it, as shown in Figure 15–50.

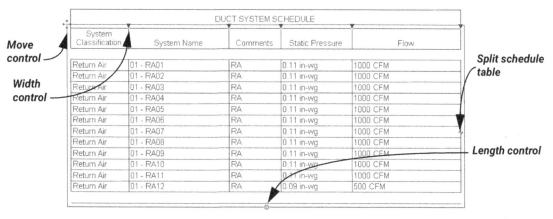

Figure 15–50

- The blue triangles modify the width of each column.

- The break mark splits the schedule into two parts.

- In a split schedule, you can use the arrows in the upper-left corner to move that portion of the schedule table. The control at the bottom of the first table changes the length of the table and impacts any connected splits, as shown in Figure 15–51.

Figure 15–51

- To unsplit a schedule, drag the Move control from the side of the schedule that you want to unsplit back to the original column.

# Split a Schedule Across Multiple Sheets

When a schedule becomes too long, you need to be able to split it and place it on multiple sheets. You can split a schedule evenly or by setting a custom height. When a schedule has been split, you can expand **Schedules/Quantities (all)** in the Project Browser to see the segments of the schedule, as shown in Figure 15–52.

**Figure 15–52**

If the split is not what you wanted, you can delete the segmented schedules from the Project Browser. Do not delete the main schedule.

## How To: Split a Schedule and Place It on Multiple Sheets

1. Make additional sheets, if needed. In a schedule view, in the *Modify Schedule/Quantities* tab>Split panel, click ▭ (Split & Place).

2. In the Split Schedule and Place on Sheets dialog box, select the sheets that you want to distribute the split schedule to, as shown in Figure 15–53.

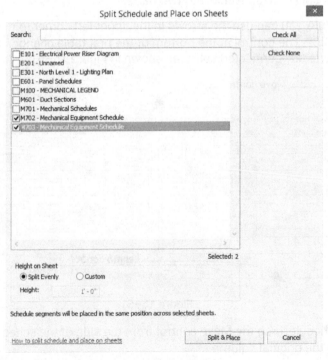

**Figure 15–53**

3. In the *Height on Sheet* section, select **Split Evenly** or **Custom**. If custom is selected, specify a *Height*.

4. Click **Split & Place**.

5. The first sheet selected in the list opens and the first segment of the split schedule is attached to your cursor. Place it on the sheet.

6. If you had selected multiple sheets in the Split Schedule and Place on Sheets dialog box, the rest of the segment schedule will automatically be placed exactly where you had initially placed the first segment of the schedule.

7. Open each sheet and use the control grips to adjust the columns and stretch the schedule to fit the sheet, as needed.

### How To: Remove Split Schedules

1. In the Project Browser, expand the schedule.

2. Select the segmented schedules and press <Delete>, or right-click and select **Delete**.

## Filter by Sheet

If you place your schedule on a sheet that has a view on it, you can filter the schedule to only display the elements that are in that viewport. In Figure 15–54, the door schedule is only showing Floor 1 doors because the sheet contains the Floor 1 - Plan view and the **Filter by sheet** option has been selected.

**Figure 15–54**

- If a view is changed or modified, the schedule and the same sheet will update accordingly.

- Schedules that are split across multiple sheets cannot use the Filter by Sheet option.

- Panel and revision schedules cannot use the Filter by Sheet option.

## How To: Filter a Schedule by Sheets

1. Open a schedule view.

2. In Properties, click **Edit...** next to *Filter*.

3. In the Schedule Properties dialog box, check the checkbox for **Filter by sheet**, as shown in Figure 15−55.

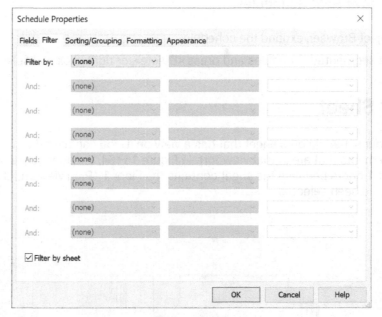

Figure 15−55

4. Click **OK**.

- You cannot use this feature if you have split the schedule.

# Practice 15d
# Work with Schedules - Mechanical/Plumbing

## Practice Objectives

- Update schedule information.
- Add a schedule to a sheet.

In this practice, you will update a schedule and place it on a sheet.

## Task 1: Fill in schedules.

1. In the practice files *Working Models>Plumbing* folder, open **Plumb-Schedules.rvt**.

2. In the Project Browser, expand **Schedules/Quantities** and open **Mechanical/Plumbing Equipment Schedule**. The schedule is already populated with some information, as shown in Figure 15–56.

| | | | | | |
|---|---|---|---|---|---|
| | | <Mechanical/Plumbing Equipment Schedule> | | | |
| A | B | C | D | E | F |
| Type Mark | Mark | Space: Name | Manufacturer | Model | Comments |
| AHU-1 | 1 | CORRIDOR | | | |
| AHU-1 | 2 | CORRIDOR | | | |
| AHU-1 | 3 | CORRIDOR | | | |
| AHU-1 | 4 | CORRIDOR | | | |
| AHU-1 | 5 | CORRIDOR | | | |
| AHU-1 | 6 | CORRIDOR | | | |
| AHU-1 | 7 | CORRIDOR | | | |
| AHU-1 | 8 | CORRIDOR | | | |
| AHU-1 | 9 | CORRIDOR | | | |
| AHU-1 | 10 | CORRIDOR | | | |
| AHU-1 | 11 | CORRIDOR | | | |
| | 49 | JNTR. | | | |
| | 50 | JNTR. | | | |
| AHU-1 | 51 | CORRIDOR | | | |
| AHU-1 | 52 | CORRIDOR | | | |

**Figure 15–56**

3. Two *Type Mark* cells are empty. Click in one of the empty *Type Mark* cells. In the *Modify Schedules/Quantities* tab>Element panel, click ▦ (Highlight in Model).

4.  In the dialog box that opens, stating there is no open view that shows any of the highlighted elements (as shown in Figure 15–57), click **OK** to search through closed views.

**Figure 15–57**

5.  In the view that comes up, if it is not showing the water heater element you need to see, click **Show**. If you can see the element, click **Close** in the Show Element(s) in View dialog box (shown in Figure 15–58).

**Figure 15–58**

6.  Zoom out so that you can see the element (e.g., a water heater) in context.

7.  In Properties, click  (Edit Type).

8.  In the Type Properties dialog box, in the *Identity Data* area, set the *Type Mark* to **HW-1**.

9.  Click **OK** to finish.

10. Return to the Mechanical/Plumbing Equipment Schedule (select the tab or press <Ctrl>+<Tab> to switch between open windows).

11. The water heaters in the project now have a *Type Mark* set, as shown in Figure 15–59.

| <Mechanical/Plumbing Equipme |||| 
| **A** | **B** | **C** | **D** |
| Type Mark | Mark | Space: Name | Manufacturer |
| AHU-1 | 1 | CORRIDOR | |
| AHU-1 | 2 | CORRIDOR | |
| AHU-1 | 3 | CORRIDOR | |
| AHU-1 | 4 | CORRIDOR | |
| AHU-1 | 5 | CORRIDOR | |
| AHU-1 | 6 | CORRIDOR | |
| AHU-1 | 7 | CORRIDOR | |
| AHU-1 | 8 | CORRIDOR | |
| AHU-1 | 9 | CORRIDOR | |
| AHU-1 | 10 | CORRIDOR | |
| AHU-1 | 11 | CORRIDOR | |
| HW-1 | 49 | JNTR. | |
| HW-1 | 50 | JNTR. | |

**Figure 15–59**

12. In the *Mark* column, you can see that the numbers are out of sequence. The numbering of the water heaters and two air handling units (AHU-1) starts at 49 and is incorrect.

13. Change the *Mark* of the incorrectly numbered AHU-1s from **51** and **52** to **12** and **13**, respectively.

14. In the schedule view, change the name of the *Manufacturer* of one of the AHUs by clicking in the cell and typing **ME Unlimited**, then clicking in another cell. An alert displays warning that changing this changes all of the elements of this type, as shown in Figure 15–60. Click **OK**.

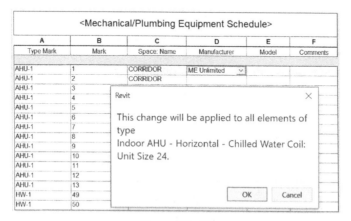

**Figure 15–60**

15. Open the Mechanical>HVAC>Floor Plans>**01 Mechanical Plan - South Wing** view.

16. Select the AHU that is connected to the Office duct system. In the Type Selector, change it to **Indoor AHU - Horizontal - Chilled Water Coil: Unit Size 12**.

    • Ignore any warnings that display.

17. While it is still selected, click **Edit Type** and set the *Type Mark* to **AHU-2**.

18. Switch back to the schedule view to see the change.

19. In the *Manufacturer* column, use the drop-down list to select the same manufacturer for the modified AHU, as shown in Figure 15–61. Click **OK** in the dialog box notifying you of the change to any other elements of that type.

| | | <Mechanical/Plumbing Equipmen | |
|---|---|---|---|
| **A** | **B** | **C** | **D** |
| Type Mark | Mark | Space: Name | Manufacturer |
| AHU-1 | 1 | CORRIDOR | ME Unlimited |
| AHU-1 | 2 | CORRIDOR | ME Unlimited |
| AHU-1 | 3 | CORRIDOR | ME Unlimited |
| AHU-1 | 4 | CORRIDOR | ME Unlimited |
| AHU-2 | 5 | CORRIDOR | |
| AHU-1 | 6 | CORRIDOR | ME Unlimited |
| AHU-1 | 7 | CORRIDOR | ME Unlimited |

Figure 15–61

20. Fill in the other information.

21. Save the project.

## Task 2: Modify the plumbing fixture schedule.

1. From the Project Browser, open the **Plumbing Fixture Schedule**. The schedule is already populated with some information.

2. Review the schedule's title and headers. Scroll down using your mouse wheel, and note that the schedule's title and headers no longer display.

3. In the *Modify Schedule/Quantities* tab>Appearance panel, select ⊞ (Freeze Header). Scroll down the schedule and note that the schedule's title and headers stay at the top.

4. In Properties, in the *Other* section, click **Edit...** next to *Sorting/Grouping*.

5. In the Schedule Properties dialog box>*Sorting/Grouping* tab, select **Type** from the Sort by: drop-down list, as shown in Figure 15–62.

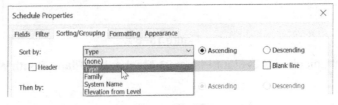

Figure 15–62

6. Select **Footer** and select **Title, count, and totals** from the drop-down list, as shown in Figure 15–63. Select the **Blank line** option and click **OK**.

**Figure 15–63**

7. Scroll through the schedule and note how it has been divided by type (e.g., family size) with space between each family type.

## Task 3: Add schedules to a sheet.

1. Open the **Duct Schedule**. Note that the different duct sizes show **<varies>** in some of the columns. This means that there are different values for these family types.

2. In the Project Browser, right-click on **Sheets (all)** and select **New Sheet**. Select the **ASCENT 30 x 42 Horizontal** title block and click **OK**.

3. In the Project Browser, right-click on the new sheet (which is bold) and select **Rename**. In the Sheet Title dialog box, set the *Number* to **M-003** and the *Name* to **Duct Schedule** and click **OK**.

4. Right-click on the Duct Schedule sheet and select **Duplicate Sheet>Duplicate Empty Sheet**, as shown in Figure 15–64. Rename it **M-004 Duct Schedule**.

**Figure 15–64**

5. Return to the Duct Schedule.

6. In Properties, click **Edit...** next to *Sorting/Grouping*.

7. In the Schedule Properties dialog box, check the box for **Itemized every instance** and click **OK**.

8.  This itemizes all the ducts and fittings in the model. Scroll down the schedule and note that this will not fit onto one sheet.

9.  In the *Modify Schedule/Quantities* tab>Split panel, click  (Split & Place).

10. In the Split Schedule and Place on Sheets dialog box, select the two Duct Schedule sheets, as shown in Figure 15–65.

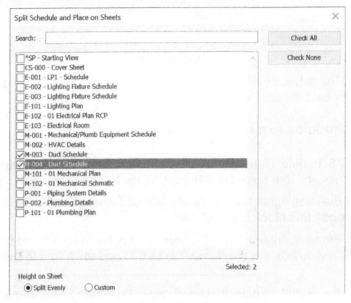

**Figure 15–65**

11. Click **Split & Place**.

12. The **M-003 - Duct Schedule** sheet automatically opens and the first segment of the split schedule is attached to your cursor. Use your mouse wheel to zoom out, if needed.

13. Place the Duct Schedule in the upper-left corner of the sheet.

14. From the Project Browser, open sheet **M-004**. Note that the other segment of the split schedule has automatically been added to the sheet in the same place as M-003.

15. The schedule will be too long and needs to be split even more.

16. Click  (Modify).

17. Go back to sheet M-003. Click on the schedule and then click  (Split Schedule Table), as shown in Figure 15–66.

**Figure 15–66**

18. Select the first section of the schedule on the sheet and use the control grips at the bottom of the schedule to stretch it to fit the sheet. On the second section of the sheet, click
   ᐯ (Split Schedule Table), as shown in Figure 15–67, to split the schedule again and use the grips to stretch or shrink the schedule to fit.

**Figure 15–67**

19. Open sheet **M-004** and adjust the schedule as needed.

**20.** Click in an empty space in the view to clear the selection.

**21.** Select the individual schedules and move them away from each other, as shown in Figure 15–68.

**Figure 15–68**

**22.** Save and close the project.

**End of practice**

# Practice 15e
# Work with Schedules - Electrical

## Practice Objectives

- Update schedule information.
- Add a schedule to a sheet.

In this practice, you will update a schedule and place it on a sheet. The model used for this practice has been modified so you can see what happens when changing elements in the sheet as well as in the views.

## Task 1: Fill in schedules.

1. In the practice files *Working Models>Electrical* folder, open **Elec-Schedules.rvt**.

2. In the Project Browser, expand *Schedules/Quantities*. Several schedules have been added to this project.

3. Double-click on **Lighting Fixture Schedule** to open it. The schedule is already populated with some of the basic information, as shown in part in Figure 15–69.

| | | | | | | Lamp | | | |
|---|---|---|---|---|---|---|---|---|---|
| A | B | C | D | E | F | G | H | | I |
| Type Mark | Description | Count | Manufacturer | Model | Lamp | Wattage | Illuminance | | Electrical Data |
| | Emergency Recessed Lighting Fixture: 2x4 - 277 | 22 | | | | 96 W | 7 fc | | Emergency 277 V/1-96 VA- 277 V/1-32 |
| L1 | Troffer Light - 2x4 Parabolic: 2'x4'(2 Lamp) - 277V | 226 | | | T-12 | 80 W | 5 fc | | 277 V/1-80 VA |
| Grand total: 248 | | | | | | | | | |

*<Lighting Fixture Schedule>*

**Figure 15–69**

4. Click in the empty *Type Mark* cell. In the *Modify Schedules/ Quantities* tab>Element panel, click  (Highlight in Model).

5. In the dialog box that opens, stating there is no open view that shows any of the highlighted elements (as shown in Figure 15–70), click **OK** to search through closed views.

**Figure 15–70**

6. In the view that comes up, if it is not showing the element you need to see, click **Show**. If you can see the element that is highlighted in the view, click **Close** in the Show Element(s) in View dialog box (shown in Figure 15–71).

**Figure 15–71**

7. In Properties, you can see that multiple emergency light fixtures are selected but display **<varies>**, as shown in Figure 15–72. More than one light fixture is selected and you cannot edit values that are grayed out.

**Figure 15–72**

8. Click  (Edit Type).

9. In the Type Properties dialog box, in the *Identity Data* section, set the *Type Mark* to **EM-1**.

10. Click **OK** to finish.

11. Return to the Lighting Fixture Schedule (select the tab or press <Ctrl>+<Tab> to switch between open windows).

12. All the emergency light fixtures in the project now have a *Type Mark* set, as shown in Figure 15–73.

| A | B | C | D | E | F | G | H | I |
|---|---|---|---|---|---|---|---|---|
| | | | | | | Lamp | | |
| Type Mark | Description | Count | Manufacturer | Model | Lamp | Wattage | Illuminance | Electrical Data |
| EM-1 | Emergency Recessed Lighting Fixture: 2x4 - 277 | 22 | | | | 96 W | 7 fc | Emergency 277 V/1-96 VA- 277 V/1-32 |
| L1 | Troffer Light - 2x4 Parabolic: 2'x4'(2 Lamp) - 277V | 226 | | | T-12 | 80 W | 5 fc | 277 V/1-80 VA |

<Lighting Fixture Schedule>

**Figure 15–73**

13. For the L1 light fixtures, in the *Manufacturer* column, type **ME Unlimited**. A dialog box displays, as shown in Figure 15–74, letting you know all of the same elements will be changed. Click **OK**. The manufacturer is added to all of the Troffer light fixtures.

**Figure 15–74**

14. Save the project.

## Task 2: Add a schedule to a sheet.

1. In the Project Browser, right-click on **Sheets (all)** and select **New Sheet**. Select the **ASCENT 30 x 42 Horizontal** title block and click **OK**.

2. In the Project Browser, right-click on the new sheet (which is bold) and select **Rename**. In the Sheet Title dialog box, set the *Number* to **E-002** and the *Name* to **Lighting Fixture Schedule**, and click **OK**.

3. Create another sheet by right-clicking on the light fixture schedule sheet and selecting **Duplicate Sheet>Duplicate Empty Sheet**, as shown in Figure 15–75. Rename it **E-003 Lighting Fixture Schedule**.

**Figure 15–75**

4. Open the Lighting Fixture Schedule.

5. In Properties, click **Edit...** next to *Sorting/Grouping*.

6. In the Schedule Properties dialog box, uncheck **Grand Totals** and check the box for **Itemized every instance** and click **OK**.

7. This itemizes all the light fixtures in the model. Scroll down the schedule and note that this will not fit onto one sheet.

8. In the *Modify Schedule/Quantities* tab>Split panel, click (Split & Place).

9. In the Split Schedule and Place on Sheets dialog box, select the two Lighting Fixture Schedule sheets, as shown in Figure 15–76.

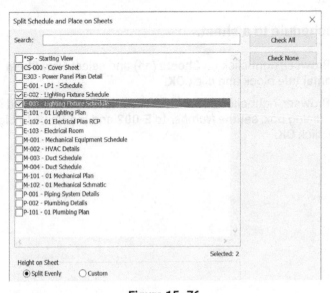

**Figure 15–76**

10. Click **Split & Place**.

11. The **E-002 - Lighting Fixture Schedule** sheet automatically opens and the first segment of the split schedule is attached to your cursor. Use your mouse wheel to zoom out, if needed.

12. Place the light fixture schedule in the upper-left corner of the sheet.

13. From the Project Browser, open sheet **E-003**. Note that the other segment of the split schedule has automatically been added to the sheet in the same place as E-002.

    • The schedule will be too long and needs to be split even more.

14. Click 🔍 (Modify).

15. Go back to sheet E-002. Click on the schedule and then click ᰍ (Split Schedule Table), as shown in Figure 15−77.

**Figure 15−77**

16. Select the first section of the schedule on the sheet and use the control grips at the bottom of the schedule to stretch it to fit the sheet. On the second section of the sheet, click ⤴ (Split Schedule Table), as shown in Figure 15–78, to split the schedule again and use the grips to stretch or shrink the schedule to fit.

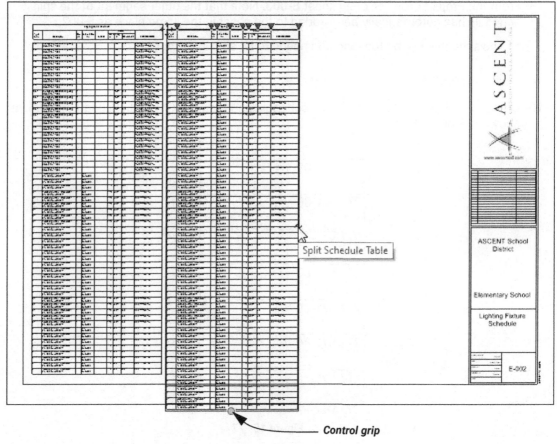

Figure 15–78

17. Click in an empty space in the view to clear the selection.

**18.** Select the individual schedules and move them away from each other, as shown in Figure 15–79.

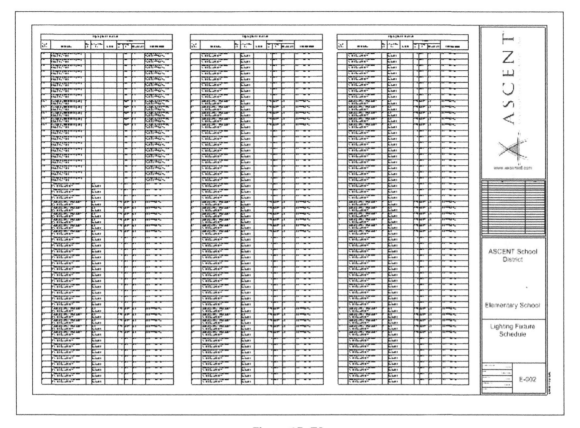

**Figure 15–79**

**19.** Open sheet **E-003** and adjust the schedule as needed.

**20.** Save and close the project.

**End of practice**

# Chapter Review Questions

1. You can tag in a 3D view, but you first have to do what to the view?

   a. You cannot tag in a 3D view.

   b. Rename the view.

   c. Lock the view.

   d. Unlock the view.

2. Which of the following elements cannot be tagged using **Tag by Category**?

   a. Spaces

   b. Ducts

   c. Plumbing Fixtures

   d. Communication Devices

3. What happens when you delete an air terminal in a Revit model?

   a. You must delete the air terminal on the sheet.

   b. You must delete the air terminal from the schedule.

   c. The air terminal is removed from the model, but not from the schedule.

   d. The air terminal is removed from the model and the schedule.

4. In a schedule, if you change type information (such as a Type Mark), all instances of that type update with the new information.

   a. True

   b. False

5. You cannot remove split schedules once they have been created.

   a. True

   b. False

# Command Summary

| Button | Command | Location |
|--------|---------|----------|
| | **Freeze Header** | • **Ribbon:** *Modify Schedule/Quantities* tab>Titles & Header panel |
| | **Highlight in Model** | • **Ribbon:** *Modify Schedule/Quantities* tab>Element panel |
| | **Material Tag** | • **Ribbon:** *Annotate* tab>Tag panel |
| | **Multi-Category** | • **Ribbon:** *Annotate* tab>Tag panel |
| | **Stair Tread/Riser Number** | • **Ribbon:** *Annotate* tab>Tag panel |
| | **Tag All Not Tagged** | • **Ribbon:** *Annotate* tab>Tag panel |
| | **Tag by Category** | • **Ribbon:** *Annotate* tab>Tag panel<br>• **Shortcut: TG** |

# Chapter 16

# Creating Details

Creating details is a critical part of the design process, as it is the step where you specify the exact information that is required to build a construction project. The elements that you can add to a model include detail components, detail lines, text, tags, symbols, and filled regions. Details can be created from views in the model, but you can also add 2D details in separate views.

## Learning Objectives

- Create drafting views where you can add 2D details.
- Add detail components that show the typical elements in a detail.
- Annotate details using detail lines, text, tags, symbols, and patterns that define materials.

# 16.1 Setting Up Detail Views

Most of the work you do in Revit is exclusively with *smart* elements that interconnect and work together in the model. However, the software does not automatically display how elements should be built to fit together. For this, you need to create detail drawings, as shown in Figure 16–1.

> **Note:** *Details are created either in 2D drafting views or in callouts from plan, elevation, or section views.*

WATER SOURCE HEAT PUMP
PIPING DETAIL

Figure 16–1

### How To: Create a Drafting View

1. In the *View* tab>Create panel, click 🖶 (Drafting View).
2. In the New Drafting View dialog box, enter a *Name* and set a *Scale*, as shown in Figure 16–2.

Figure 16–2

3. Click **OK**. A blank view is created with space in which you can sketch the detail.

   *Note: Drafting views are listed in their own section in the Project Browser.*

## How To: Create a Detail View from Model Elements

1. Start the **Section** or **Callout** command.
2. In the Type Selector, select the **Detail View: Detail** type.
   - The marker indicates that it is a detail, as shown for a section in Figure 16–3.

**Figure 16–3**

3. Place the section or a callout of the area you want to use for the detail.

   *Note: Callouts also have a Detail View type that can be used in the same way.*

4. Open the new detail.
- Change the detail level to see more or less of the element materials.
- Use the **Detail Line** tool to sketch on top of or add to the building elements.

- Because you are working with smart elements, a detail of the model is a true representation. When the building elements change, the detail changes as well, as shown in Figure 16–4.

**Before**    **After - Sink size changed**

**Figure 16–4**

- You can create detail elements on top of the model and then toggle the model off so that it does not show in the detail view. In Properties, in the *Graphics* section, change *Display Model* to **Do not display**. You can also set the model to **Halftone**, as shown in Figure 16–5.

**Figure 16–5**

# Referencing a Drafting View

Once you have created a drafting view, you can reference it in another view (such as a callout, elevation, or section view), as shown in Figure 16–6. For example, in a section view, you might want to reference an existing roof detail. You can reference drafting views, sections, elevations, and callouts.

**Figure 16–6**

- You can use the search feature to limit the information displayed.

## How To: Reference a Drafting View

1. Open the view in which you want to place the reference.
2. Start the **Section**, **Callout**, or **Elevation** command.
3. In the *Modify* contextual tab>Reference panel, select **Reference Other View**.
4. In the drop-down list, select **<New Drafting View>** or an existing drafting view.
5. Place the view marker.
6. When you place the associated drafting view on a sheet, the marker in this view updates with the appropriate information.

- If you select **<New Drafting View>** from the drop-down list, a new view is created in the *Drafting Views (Detail)* area in the Project Browser. You can rename it as needed. The new view does not include any model elements.

- When you create a detail based on a section, elevation, or callout, you do not need to link it to a drafting view.

- You can change a referenced view to a different view. Select the view marker and in the ribbon, select the new view from the list.

# Saving Drafting Views

To create a library of standard details, save the non-model specific drafting views to your server. They can then be imported into a project and modified to suit. They are saved as .RVT files.

Drafting views can be saved in two ways:

- Save an individual drafting view to a new file.
- Save all of the drafting views as a group in one new file.

## How To: Save One Drafting View to a File

1. In the Project Browser, right-click on the drafting view you want to save and select **Save to New File...**, as shown in Figure 16–7.

**Figure 16–7**

2. In the Save As dialog box, specify a name and location for the file and click **Save**.

## How To: Save a Group of Drafting Views to a File

*Note: You can save sheets, drafting views, model views (floor plans), schedules, and reports.*

1. In the *File* tab, expand 💾 (Save As), expand 📖 (Library), and then click 🖼 (View).
2. In the Save Views dialog box, in the *Views:* area, expand the list and select **Show drafting views only**.
3. Select the drafting views that you want to save, as shown in Figure 16–8.

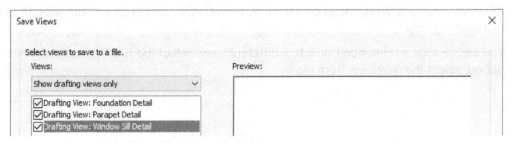

**Figure 16–8**

4. Click **OK**.

5. In the Save As dialog box, specify a name and location for the file and click **Save**.

## How To: Use a Saved Drafting View in Another Project

1. Open the project to which you want to add the drafting view.

2. In the *Insert* tab>Load from Library panel, expand  (Insert from File) and click  (Insert Views from File).

3. In the Open dialog box, select the project in which you saved the detail and click **Open**.

4. In the Insert Views dialog box, limit the types of views to **Show drafting views only**, as shown in Figure 16–9.

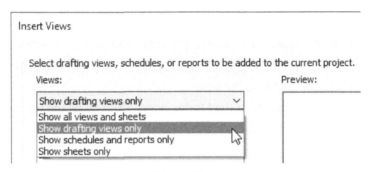

**Figure 16–9**

5. Select the view(s) that you want to insert and click **OK**.

---

### 💡 Hint: Importing Details from Other CAD Software

You might already have a set of standard details created in a different CAD program, such as the AutoCAD® software. You can reuse the details in Revit by importing them into a temporary project. Once you have imported the detail, it helps to clean it up and save it as a view before bringing it into your active project.

1. In a new project, create a drafting view and make it active.

2. In the *Insert* tab>Import panel, click 🔲 (Import CAD).

3. In the Import CAD dialog box, select the file to import. Most of the default values are what you need. You might want to change the *Layer/Level colors* to **Black and White**.

4. Click **Open**.

- If you want to modify the detail, select the imported data. In the *Modify | [filename]* tab>Import Instance panel, expand 📦 (Explode) and click 📦 (Partial Explode) or 📦 (Full Explode). Click 📦× (Delete Layers) before you explode the detail. A full explode greatly increases the file size.

- Modify the detail using tools in the Modify panel. Change all the text and line styles to Revit-specific elements.

# 16.2 Adding Detail Components

Revit elements, typically require additional information to ensure that they are constructed correctly. To create details such as the one shown in Figure 16–10, you add detail components, detail lines, and various annotation elements.

- Detail elements are not directly connected to the model, even if model elements display in the view.

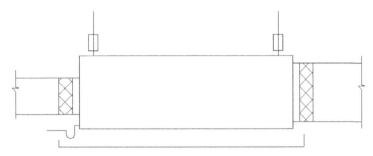

**Figure 16–10**

- If you want to draw detail lines in 3D, use the **Model Line** tool. Detail Line is grayed out when you are in a 3D view or perspective view.

## Detail Components

Detail components are families made of 2D and annotation elements. Over 500 detail components organized by CSI format are found in the *Detail Items* folder of the Revit Library, as shown in Figure 16–11.

**Figure 16–11**

*Note: For more information on how to load detail items using the Load Autodesk Family dialog box, see 4.2 Loading Components.*

- You can also access Detail Items from the Load Autodesk Family dialog box, as shown in Figure 16–12.

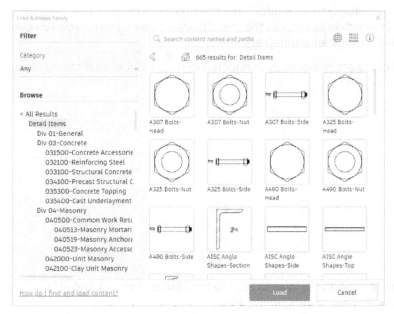

**Figure 16–12**

## How To: Add a Detail Component

1. In the *Annotate* tab>Detail panel, expand ⊞ (Component) and click ⊞ (Detail Component).

2. In the Type Selector, select the detail component type. You can load additional types from the Revit Library.

3. Many detail components can be rotated as you insert them by pressing <Spacebar>. Alternatively, select **Rotate after placement** in the Options Bar, as shown in Figure 16–13.

**Figure 16–13**

4. Place the component in the view.

# Adding Break Lines

The break line is a detail component found in the Revit Library's *Detail Items\Div 01-General* folder. It consists of a rectangular area (shown highlighted in Figure 16−14) that is used to block out elements behind it. You can modify the size of the area that is covered and change the size of the cut line using the controls.

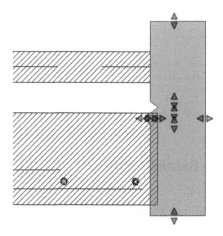

Figure 16−14

> ### Hint: Working with the Draw Order of Details
>
> When you select detail elements in a view, you can change the draw order of the elements in the *Modify | Detail Items* tab>Arrange panel. You can bring elements in front of other elements or place them behind elements, as shown in Figure 16−15.

Draw order: front          Draw order: back

Figure 16−15

- **(Bring to Front):** Places element in front of all other elements.

- **(Send to Back):** Places element behind all other elements.

- **(Bring Forward):** Moves element one step to the front.

- **(Send Backward):** Moves element one step to the back.

You can select multiple detail elements and change the draw order of all of them in one step. They keep the relative order of the original selection.

# Repeating Details

Instead of having to insert a component multiple times (such as brick or concrete block), you can use ⫶ (Repeating Detail Component) and create a string of components, as shown in Figure 16–16.

**Figure 16–16**

### How To: Insert a Repeating Detail Component

1. In the *Annotate* tab>Detail panel, expand ⬚ (Component) and click ⫶ (Repeating Detail Component).

2. In the Type Selector, select the detail you want to use.

3. In the Draw panel, click ╱ (Line) or ⬚ (Pick Lines).

4. In the Options Bar, type a value for the *Offset*, if needed.

5. The components repeat, as required, to fit the length of the sketched or selected line, as shown in Figure 16–17. You can lock the components to the line.

*Existing line* ⟋  ⟍ *Repeating detail*

**Figure 16–17**

**Hint:** (Insulation)

Adding batt insulation is similar to adding a repeating detail component, but instead of a series of bricks or other elements, it creates the linear batting pattern shown in Figure 16–18.

**Figure 16–18**

Before you place the insulation in the view, specify the *Offset* and other options in the Options Bar (as shown in Figure 16–19), as well as the *Width* in Properties.

Modify | Place Insulation          ☐ Chain   Offset: 0.00"          to cente ∨

**Figure 16–19**

# 16.3 Annotating Details

After you have added components and sketched detail lines, you need to add annotations to the detail view. You can place text notes and dimensions, as shown in Figure 16–20, as well as symbols and tags. Filled regions are used to add hatching.

**FLOOR DRAIN**

**FINISHED FLOOR ON THINSET MORTAR, SLOPE TO FLOOR DRAIN. REFER TO ARCHITECTURAL DRAWINGS**

**PROVIDE WATERPROOFING MEMBRANE**

**CONCRETE FLOOR**

**TRANSITION COUPLER**

PIPE

SIZE

**Figure 16–20**

## Creating Filled Regions

Many elements include material information that displays in plan and section views, while other elements need more details to be added. For example, the concrete wall shown in Figure 16–21 includes material information, while the earth to the left of the wall needs to be added using the **Filled Region** command.

*Added filled region*

*Wall material already inside the wall*

**Figure 16–21**

The patterns used in details are *drafting patterns*. They are scaled to the view scale and update if you modify it. You can also add full-size *model patterns*, such as a Flemish Bond brick pattern, to the surface of some elements.

## How To: Add a Filled Region

1. In the *Annotate* tab>Detail panel, expand ▦ (Region) and click ▦ (Filled Region).
2. Create a closed boundary using the Draw tools.
3. In the Line Style panel, select the line style for the outside edge of the boundary. If you do not want the boundary to display, select the **<Invisible lines>** style.
4. In the Type Selector, select the fill type, as shown in Figure 16–22.

**Figure 16–22**

5. Click ✓ (Finish Edit Mode).

• You can modify a region by changing the fill type in the Type Selector or by editing the sketch.

• Double-click on the edge of the filled region to edit the sketch. If you have the Selection option set to ▨ (Select elements by face), you can select the pattern.

### 🔆 Hint: Creating a Filled Region Pattern Type

You can create a custom pattern by duplicating and editing an existing pattern type.

1. Select an existing region or create a boundary.

2. In Properties, click ⊞ (Edit Type).

3. In the Type Properties dialog box, click **Duplicate** and name the new pattern.

4. Select the *Foreground/Background Fill Pattern* and *Color* and specify the *Line Weight* and *Masking*, as shown in Figure 16–23.

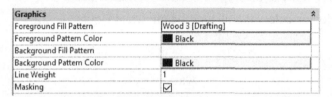

Figure 16–23

5. Click **OK**.

- You can select from two types of fill patterns: **Drafting** (as shown in Figure 16–24) and **Model**. Drafting fill patterns scale to the view scale factor. Model fill patterns display full scale on the model.

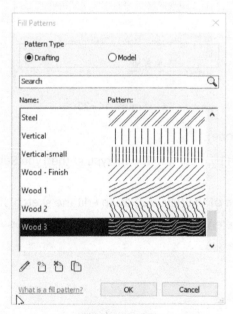

Figure 16–24

# Adding Detail Tags

Besides adding text to a detail, you can tag detail components using $\square^{①}$ (Tag By Category). The tag name is set in the Type Parameters for that component, as shown in Figure 16–25. This means that if you have more than one copy of the component in your project, you do not have to rename it each time you place its tag.

*Note: The **Detail Item Tag.rfa** tag is located in the Annotations folder in the Revit Library.*

Figure 16–25

- For more information on annotating using keynotes see *B.6 Keynoting and Keynote Legends*.

# Linework

To emphasize a particular line or change the look of a line in elevations and other views, modify the lines with the **Linework** command. Changes made to lines with the **Linework** command are view-specific, applying only to the view in which you make them.

- The **Linework** command can be used on project edges of model elements, cut edges of model elements, edges in imported CAD files, and edges in linked Revit models.

- You cannot use the **Linework** command to change the line style of annotation lines like a dimension line or leader line.

## How To: Adjust Linework

1. In the *Modify* tab>View panel, click ⟨icon⟩ (Linework), or type the shortcut **LW**.

2. In the *Modify | Linework* tab>Line Style panel, select the line style you want to use from the list.

3. Move the cursor and highlight the line you want to change. You can use <Tab> to toggle through the lines as needed.

4. Click on the line to change it to the new line style.

5. Click on other lines as needed or click ⟨icon⟩ (Modify) to end the command

- If the line is too long or short, you can modify the length using the controls at the end of the line.

# Practice 16a
# Create a Fire Damper Detail - Mechanical

## Practice Objectives

- Create a drafting view.
- Add filled regions, detail components, and annotations.

In this practice, you will create a drafting view. In the new view you will add detail lines of different weights, insulation, and filled regions. You will also add detail components, including break lines and text notes. Finally, you will place the detail view on a sheet (as shown in Figure 16–26) and place a reference section.

**Figure 16–26**

- It is recommended that you also complete the other Detail practices if time permits, even though they are not for your specific discipline.

## Task 1: Create a drafting view.

1. In the practice files *Working Models>Mechanical* folder, open **Mech-Detailing.rvt**.

2. In the *View* tab>Create panel, click (Drafting View).

3. In the New Drafting View dialog box, set the following:

- *Name*: **Fire Damper Detail**
- *Scale*: **1 1/2"=1'-0"**

4. In Properties, change *Discipline* to **Mechanical** and *Sub-Discipline* to **HVAC**. The new view moves to that node in the Project Browser.

## Task 2: Draw detail lines.

1. In the *Annotate* tab>Detail panel, click ⬜ (Detail Line).

2. In the *Modify | Place Detail Lines* tab, set the *Line Style* to **Thin Lines** and make sure **Chain** is unchecked. Draw the two vertical lines shown in Figure 16–27.

3. Change the *Line Style* to **Wide Lines** and draw the two horizontal lines shown in Figure 16–27. These become the primary duct and wall lines.

- If the difference in the line weights does not display clearly, zoom in and, in the Quick

   Access Toolbar, toggle off ⬛ (Thin Lines).

*Note: The dimensions are for information only.*

Figure 16–27

4. Continue adding and modifying detail lines to create the elements shown in Figure 16–28. Use modify commands (such as **Split** and **Offset**) and the draw tools.

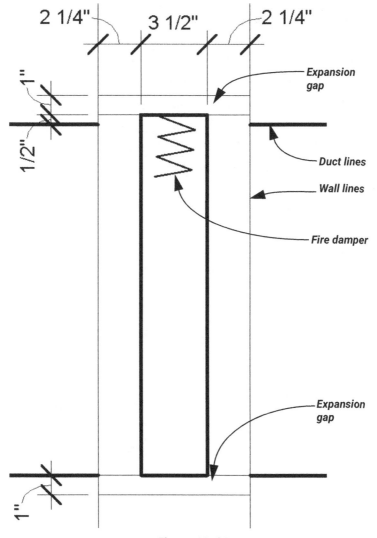

**Figure 16–28**

5. Save the project.

## Task 3:  Add detail components.

1.  In the *Annotate* tab>Detail panel, expand ⬚ (Component) and select ⬚ (Detail Component).

2.  In the Type Selector, select **AISC Angle Shapes - Section L3X2X1/4**.

3.  Place the angle on the top left, as shown in Figure 16−29.

    *   Press <Spacebar> to rotate the angle before placing it.

4.  Change the type to **AISC Angle Shapes - Section L2X2X1/4** and place the angle on the bottom of the duct, as shown in Figure 16−29.

5.  Select the two angle components and mirror them to the other side, as shown in Figure 16−29.

*1. Place L3X2X1/4*

*3. Mirror both angles*

*2. Place L2X2X1/4*

**Figure 16−29**

6. Add four break line components. Rotate and use the controls to modify the size until all of your excess lines are covered, as shown in Figure 16–30.

   *Note: The exact location and size of your break lines might vary.*

**Figure 16–30**

7. Save the project.

## Task 4: Add insulation and filled regions.

1. In the *Annotate* tab>Detail panel, click ⊗ (Insulation).
2. In Properties, set the *Insulation Width* to **1"**.
3. Draw the insulation lines in the two expansion gaps, as shown in Figure 16–31.
4. In the *Annotate* tab>Detail panel, expand ▨ (Region) and click ▨ (Filled Region).
5. In the Type Selector, select **Filled region: Diagonal Down**.

6. Draw rectangles around the wall areas as shown in Figure 16–31.

7. Click ✔ (Finish). The filled regions display.

   *Note: The filled region pattern does not display until you finish the process.*

**Filled regions** — ⟵ — **Insulation**

**Figure 16–31**

8. Save the project.

## Task 5: Add text notes.

1. In the *Annotate* tab>Text panel, click **A** (Text).

2. In the *Modify | Place Text* tab>Leader panel, select ⤺**A** (Two Segments) as the leader style.

3. In the Type Selector, select **Text: Note 3/32"**.

**4.** Add text notes, as shown in Figure 16–32.

WALL CONSTRUCTION,
SEE ARCHITECTURAL
DWGS

EXPANSION GAP TO BE
FILLED WITH MINERAL WOOL

SUPPORT ANGLE (TYP)

ACCORDION FOLD
FIRE DAMPER

DUCT

**Figure 16–32**

**5.** Save the project.

## Task 6: Place the detail on a sheet and reference it in the project.

**1.** In the Project Browser, open the sheet **M-002 - HVAC Details**.

**2.** In the Project Browser, drag the **Fire Damper Detail** view to the sheet.

**3.** Open the Mechanical>HVAC>**01 - Mechanical Plan** view.

**4.** Zoom in on one of the duct systems.

**5.** In the *View* tab>Create panel, click ⌀ (Callout).

**6.** In the *Modify | Callout* tab>Reference panel, select **Reference Other View**.

7. Expand the drop-down list and select the new **Fire Damper Detail**, as shown in Figure 16–33.

8. Place the callout at the intersection of a duct and the wall, as shown in Figure 16–33. The information is filled out based on the location of the detail view on the sheet.

**Figure 16–33**

9. Click ⤢ (Modify).

10. Double-click on the callout head, and note that the Fire Damper Detail drafting view becomes the active view. This is because the callout is now linked to this drafting view.

11. Save and close the project.

**End of practice**

# Practice 16b
# Create a Meter Pedestal Detail - Electrical

## Practice Objective

- Create and annotate details.

In this practice, you will create a detail using detail lines and filled regions. You will then annotate the detail with text and dimensions, as shown in Figure 16-34.

## METER PEDESTAL - UG SERVICE
## 1 PHASE & 3 PHASE ALL VOLTAGES
## SERVICE SIZE: 600 AMP MAXIMUM

**Figure 16-34**

- It is recommended that you also complete the other Detail practices if time permits, even though they are not for your specific discipline.

## Task 1:  Create a drafting view.

1.  In the practice files *Working Models>Electrical* folder, open **Elec-Detailing.rvt**.

2.  In the *View* tab>Create panel, click ⊟ (Drafting View).

3.  In the New Drafting View dialog box, set the name and scale as follows:

    - *Name*: **Electrical Meter Pedestal Detail**

    - *Scale*: **1 1/2"=1'-0"**

4.  In Properties, change *Discipline* to **Electrical** and *Sub-Discipline* to **Power**. The new view moves to that node in the Project Browser.

## Task 2:  Draw detail lines.

1.  In the *Annotate* tab>Detail panel, click ⬙ (Detail Line).

2.  In the *Modify | Place Detail Lines* tab, set the *Line Style* to **Wide Lines** and draw the meter box shown in Figure 16–35. As you draw, make sure **Chain** is checked or unchecked, as needed.

3.  Change the *Line Style* to **Medium Lines** and draw the meter circle, as shown in Figure 16–35.

    - If the difference in the line weights does not display clearly, zoom in and toggle off

      ⧉ (Thin Lines) in the Quick Access Toolbar.

*The dimensions in the image are for information only.*

**Figure 16–35**

4.  Continue adding and modifying detail lines to create the PVC conduit, meter pedestal, wire, wire clips, and grounding rod shown in Figure 16−36. Use Modify commands (such as **Copy** and **Offset**) and the draw tools.

**Figure 16−36**

5.  Create a side view of the meter using reference planes as your trajectory lines, as shown in Figure 16−37. When you are finished, you can delete the reference planes and select the elements and move them over so there is room for labels.

**Figure 16–37**

6.  Save the project.

## Task 3: Add detail components.

1.  In the *Annotate* tab>Detail panel, expand  (Component) and select  (Detail Component).
2.  In the Type Selector, select **Break Line**.
3.  Add a break line to the bottom of both grounding rods. Rotate and use the controls to modify the size until all of your excess lines are covered, as shown in Figure 16–38.

    *Note: The exact location and size of your break lines might vary.*

**Figure 16–38**

4.  Save the project.

## Task 4: Add filled regions.

1. Draw a reference plane **1'-0 3/4"** from the bottom of the post as shown in Figure 16–39 to help with drawing the finished grade.

**Figure 16–39**

2. In the *Annotate* tab>Detail panel, expand ▨ (Region) and click ▨ (Filled Region).

3. In the Type Selector, select **Filled region: Earth**.

4. Set the *Line Style* to **Medium Lines**.

5. Use the different line tools to draw the finished grade areas, as shown in Figure 16–40.

6. Click ✔ (Finish). The filled regions display.

7. Start the **Filled Region** command again and draw areas for the concrete, as shown in Figure 16–40.

*Note: The filled region pattern does not display until you finish the process.*

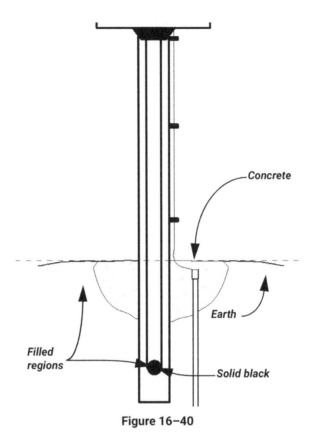

**Figure 16–40**

8.  Save the project.

## Task 5:  Add text notes.

1.  In the *Annotate* tab>Text panel, click **A** (Text).

2.  In the *Modify | Place Text* tab>Leader panel, select <sup>A</sup> (Two Segments) as the leader style.

3.  In the Type Selector, select **Text: Note 3/32"**.

4.  Add text notes, as shown in Figure 16–41.

METER SOCKET

METER

METER PEDESTAL TO BE SET IN
CONCRETE SHALL BE CENTERED IN A
12" X 12" X 12" AREA

SCH. 40 PVC CONDUIT

FINISHED GRADE

WARNING TAPE

GROUNDING ROD IN
ACCORDANCE WITH NEC AND
LOCAL INSPECTION AUTHORITY
REQUIREMENTS

90° ELBOW (24" RADIUS
MIN.)

CONDUIT MAINTAINED BY UTILITY

CONDUIT MAINTAINED BY
CUSTOMER FOR ALL SERVICES

**Figure 16–41**

5.  Save the project.

## Task 6: Place the detail on a sheet and reference it in the project.

1.  In the Project Browser, open the sheet **E-004 - Meter Details**.
2.  In the Project Browser, drag the **Electrical Meter Pedestal Detail** view to the sheet.
3.  Open the Electrical>Power>Floor Plans>**01- Power Plan** view.
4.  Zoom in on the north wing above the electrical room.
5.  In the *View* tab>Create panel, click ⌀ (Callout).
6.  In the *Modify | Callout* tab>Reference panel, select **Reference Other View**.

7. Expand the drop-down list and select the new **Electrical Meter Pedestal Detail**, as shown in Figure 16–42.

8. Place the callout at the exterior wall, as shown in Figure 16–42. The information is filled out based on the location of the detail view on the sheet.

**Figure 16–42**

9. Click ⌖ (Modify).

10. Double-click on the callout head, and note that the Electrical Meter Pedestal Detail drafting view becomes the active view. This is because the callout is now linked to this drafting view.

11. Save and close the project.

**End of practice**

# Practice 16c
# Create a Floor Drain Detail - Plumbing

## Practice Objective

- Create and annotate details.

In this practice, you will create a floor drain detail using detail components. You will then annotate the floor drain detail with text and a dimension, as shown in Figure 16–43.

FLOOR DRAIN

FINISHED FLOOR ON THINSET MORTAR, SLOPE TO FLOOR DRAIN. REFER TO ARCHITECTURAL DRAWINGS

PROVIDE WATERPROOFING MEMBRANE

CONCRETE FLOOR

TRANSITION COUPLER

PIPE
SIZE

**Figure 16–43**

- It is recommended that you also complete the other Detail practices if time permits, even though they are not for your specific discipline.

## Task 1: Create a drafting view.

1. In the practice files *Working Models>Plumbing* folder, open **Plumb-Detailing.rvt**.

2. In the *View* tab>Create panel, click ▭ (Drafting View).

3. In the New Drafting View dialog box, set the name and scale as follows:

- *Name*: **Floor Drain Detail**
- *Scale*: **3"=1'-0"**

**4.** In Properties, change *Discipline* to **Plumbing** and *Sub-Discipline* to **Plumbing**. The new view moves to that node in the Project Browser.

## Task 2: Add detail components.

**1.** In the *Annotate* tab>Detail panel, expand ▣ (Component) and select ▣ (Detail Component).

**2.** In the Type Selector, select **Slab with Optional Haunch-Section 4"** and draw it so the length is **2'-3 1/4"**, as shown in Figure 16−44.

**3.** Start the **Detail Component** command again and add **Floor Drain - Section** at the center of the slab and **Resilient Flooring - Section** drawn on both sides of the drain out to the edge of the slab, as shown in Figure 16−44. (Dimension in figure is for reference only.)

**Figure 16−44**

**4.** Start the **Detail Component** command again and add three break line components. Rotate and use the controls to modify the size until all of your excess lines are covered, as shown in Figure 16−45. The break lines need to hide the portion of the detail components that you do not want shown.

**Figure 16−45**

**5.** Save the project.

## Task 3: Add grout and filled regions.

1. In the *Annotate* tab>Detail panel, expand **Region** and click ▨ (Filled Region).
2. In the Type Selector, select **Filled region: Grout**.
3. Draw lines around the areas between the drain and the floor, as shown in Figure 16–46.

   *Note: The filled region pattern does not display until you finish the process.*

*Filled regions*

**Figure 16–46**

4. Click ✓ (Finish). The filled regions display.
5. Repeat the **Filled Region** command on the other side of the drain.
6. Save the project.

## Task 4: Add text notes.

1. In the *Annotate* tab>Text panel, click **A** (Text).
2. In the *Modify | Place Text* tab>Leader panel, select ⤺**A** (Two Segments) as the leader style.
3. In the Type Selector, select **Text: Note 3/32"**.

**4.** Add text notes, as shown in Figure 16−47.

FLOOR DRAIN

FINISHED FLOOR ON THINSET
MORTAR, SLOPE TO FLOOR
DRAIN REFER TO
ARCHITECTURAL DRAWINGS

PROVIDE WATERPROOFING MEMBRANE

CONCRETE FLOOR

TRANSITION COUPLER

**Figure 16−47**

**5.** Save the project.

## Task 5: Place the detail on a sheet and reference it in the project.

**1.** In the Project Browser, open the sheet **P-003 - Floor Drain Details**.

**2.** In the Project Browser, drag the **Floor Drain Detail** view to the sheet.

**3.** Open the Plumbing>Sanitary>**01- Sanitary Plan** view.

**4.** Zoom in on the kitchen in the upper-right side of the building.

**5.** In the *View* tab>Create panel, click ⊘ (Callout).

**6.** In the *Modify | Callout* tab>Reference panel, select **Reference Other View**.

7. Expand the drop-down list and select the new **Floor Drain Detail**, as shown in Figure 16–48.

8. Place the callout at the intersection of a duct and the wall, as shown in Figure 16–48. The information is filled out based on the location of the detail view on the sheet.

**Figure 16–48**

9. Click (Modify).

10. Double-click on the callout head, and note that the Floor Drain Detail drafting view becomes the active view. This is because the callout is now linked to this drafting view.

11. Save and close the project.

**End of practice**

# Chapter Review Questions

1. Which of the following are ways in which you can create a detail? (Select all that apply.)

   a. Make a callout of a section and sketch over it.

   b. Draw all of the elements from scratch.

   c. Import a CAD detail and modify or sketch over it.

   d. Insert an existing drafting view from another file.

2. In which type of view (access shown in Figure 16–49) can you NOT add detail lines?

**Figure 16–49**

   a. Plans

   b. Elevations

   c. 3D views

   d. Legends

3. How are detail components different from building components?

   a. There is no difference.

   b. Detail components are made of 2D lines and annotations only.

   c. Detail components are made of building elements, but only display in detail views.

   d. Detail components are made of 2D and 3D elements.

4. Which of the following statements is true when you sketch detail lines?

   a. Always the same width.

   b. Vary in width according to the view.

   c. Display in all views associated with the detail.

   d. Display only in the view in which they were created.

**5.** Which command do you use to add a pattern (such as concrete or earth, as shown in Figure 16–50) to part of a detail?

Concrete

Earth

**Figure 16–50**

a. Region

b. Filled Region

c. Masking Region

d. Pattern Region

# Command Summary

| Button | Command | Location |
|---|---|---|
| **CAD Import Tools** | | |
| | Delete Layers | • **Ribbon:** *Modify | <imported filename>* tab>Import Instance panel |
| | Full Explode | • **Ribbon:** *Modify | <imported filename>* tab>Import Instance panel, expand Explode |
| | Import CAD | • **Ribbon:** *Insert* tab>Import panel |
| | Partial Explode | • **Ribbon:** *Modify | <imported filename>* tab>Import Instance panel, expand Explode |
| **Detail Tools** | | |
| | Detail Component | • **Ribbon:** *Annotate* tab>Detail panel, expand Component |
| | Detail Line | • **Ribbon:** *Annotate* tab>Detail panel |
| | Insulation | • **Ribbon:** *Annotate* tab>Detail panel |
| | Filled Region | • **Ribbon:** *Annotate* tab>Detail panel |
| | Repeating Detail Component | • **Ribbon:** *Annotate* tab>Detail panel, expand Component |
| **View Tools** | | |
| | Bring Forward | • **Ribbon:** *Modify | Detail Items* tab>Arrange panel |
| | Bring to Front | • **Ribbon:** *Modify | Detail Items* tab>Arrange panel |
| | Drafting View | • **Ribbon:** *View* tab>Create panel |
| | Insert from File: Insert Views from File | • **Ribbon:** *Insert* tab>Load from Library panel, expand Insert from File |
| | Send Backward | • **Ribbon:** *Modify | Detail Items* tab>Arrange panel |
| | Send to Back | • **Ribbon:** *Modify | Detail Items* tab>Arrange panel |

# Additional Tools for Design Development

There are many other tools available in Revit® that you can use when creating and working in models. This appendix provides details about several tools and commands that are related to those covered in the Design Development section of this guide.

## Learning Objectives

- Purge unused component elements to increase the processing speed of the model.
- Customize building type settings for heating and cooling loads.
- Define color schemes.
- Create custom ducts and piping types.
- Modify system graphics using filters and overrides.
- Understand worksharing and working with workset-related files.

# A.1 Purging Unused Elements

To reduce file size and remove unused elements from a project, including individual component types, you can purge the project, as shown in Figure A–1.

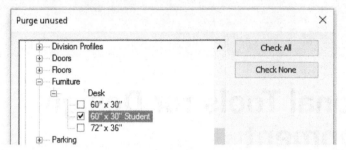

**Figure A–1**

- Some elements are nested in other elements and it might require several rounds of purging the project to remove them.

## How To: Purge Unused Elements

1. In the *Manage* tab>Settings panel, click (Purge Unused).
2. In the Purge unused dialog box, click **Check None** and select the elements you want to purge.
3. Click **OK**.

- Purging unused components helps simplify the list of families loaded in a project.

# A.2 Building Type Settings

For even more control over Heating and Cooling Load analysis, you can customize the Building Types using the Building/Space and Type Settings dialog box, as shown in Figure A–2.

* To open the dialog box, in the *Manage* tab>Settings panel, expand ▦ (MEP Settings) and click 🔧 (Building/Space and Type Settings), or in the *Analyze* tab, click ↘ in the Reports & Schedules panel title.

**Figure A–2**

* You can add, duplicate, rename and delete Building and Space Types.

- For each type of building or space you can specify energy analysis information, such as the number of people and expected heat gain per person, as well as the schedules of typical times that the building is occupied, as shown for a Warehouse in Figure A–3.

  - To get to the Schedule Settings dialog box, click on a Building Type on the left, then on the right, click on Occupancy, Lighting, or Power Schedule and click within the *Value* name.

**Figure A–3**

- Building/Space type names are exported when you export a project to gbXML for further processing in other energy analysis programs.

# A.3 Defining Color Schemes

Color schemes are used with spaces, zones, ducts, and pipes. You can define colors using many of the properties connected to the elements such as the Duct Friction Color Fill, as shown in Figure A-4.

## Duct Color Fill Legend - Friction

- 0.00 in-wg/100ft
- 0.01 in-wg/100ft
- 0.02 in-wg/100ft
- 0.03 in-wg/100ft
- 0.05 in-wg/100ft
- 0.07 in-wg/100ft
- 0.08 in-wg/100ft
- 0.10 in-wg/100ft

**Figure A-4**

## How To: Define a Color Scheme

1.  In Properties, click the button next to the **Color Scheme** (for spaces and HVAC zones) or **System Color Schemes** (for pipes and ducts) parameter.

    - **Color Schemes:** For spaces and HVAC zones, in the Edit Color Scheme dialog box, *Schemes* area, select a **Category**.

    - **System Color Scheme:** For pipes and ducts, in the Color Schemes dialog box, select the *Color scheme* for either the Pipes or Ducts category. Then, in the Edit Color Scheme dialog box, select a **Category** in the *Scheme* area.

2.  Select an existing scheme and click  (Duplicate).

3.  In the New color scheme dialog box, enter a new name and click **OK**. If the Colors Not Preserved warning displays, click **OK** again.

4.  In the *Scheme Definition* area, type a name for the *Title* of the color scheme. This displays when the legend is placed in the view.

5. In the Color drop-down list, select an option, as shown in Figure A–5. The available parameters depend on the type of scheme you are creating.

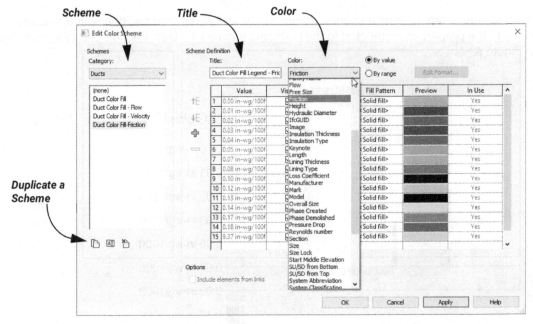

Figure A–5

6. Select the **By value** or **By range** options to set how the color scheme displays. Depending on the selection made in the Color drop-down list, **By range** might not be available.

7. If required, click ✚ (Add Value) to add more rows to the scheme, as shown in Figure A–6. Modify the visibility (*Visible* column), *Color*, and *Fill Pattern* as needed.

Figure A–6

8.  In the *Options* area, select **Include elements from linked files** if you are using linked models.

9.  Click **OK** to end the command.

## Color Schemes By Value

If you select the **By value** option, you can modify the visibility, color, and fill pattern of the scheme. The value is assigned by the parameter data in the room or area object.

*   Values are automatically updated when you add data to the parameters used in the color scheme. For example, if you create a color by space name and then add another space name in the project, it is also added to the color scheme.

*   Click ↑E (Move Rows Up) and ↓E (Move Rows Down) to change the order of rows in the list.

*   To remove a row, select it and click ▭ (Remove Value). This is only available if the parameter data is not being used in the room or area elements in the project.

## Color Schemes By Range

If you select the **By range** option, you can modify the *At Least* variable and the *Caption*, as well as the visibility, color, and fill pattern, as shown in Figure A–7.

**Figure A–7**

*   Click **Edit Format...** to modify the units display format.

*   To add rows, select the row above the new row and click

    ➕ (Add Value). The new row increments according to the previous distances set or by double the value of the first row.

# A.4 Custom Duct and Piping Types

## Duct/Pipe Types and Settings

The System and Mechanical default templates are pre-loaded with duct/pipe types and routing preferences set up. You can create additional duct/pipe types and modify the routing preferences. Ducts and pipes are system families; therefore, you need to duplicate an existing family in the Type Properties, as shown in Figure A–8.

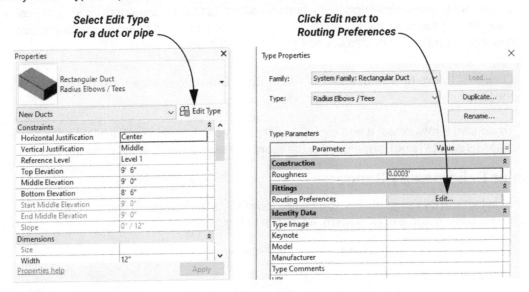

**Figure A–8**

## Routing Preferences

The Routing Preferences dialog box enables you to specify the kind of pipe and pipe fittings to use. You can have a simple pipe type with one kind of pipe segment used for all sizes and one family for each kind of pipe fitting. Alternatively, you can set up the pipe type so that as the pipe size increases, different pipe and different fittings are used. Use ✛ (Add Row) and

▬ (Remove Row) to create or remove rows, and the arrows to re-order items.

- Duct routing preferences are similar.

The Routing Preferences dialog box is shown in Figure A–9.

**Figure A–9**

- **Segments and Sizes...** enables you to create named segments with corresponding standard pipe sizes.

- **Load Family...** enables you to load additional pipe fittings if needed.

# A.5 Work with System Graphics

Default system colors are set up by graphic overrides at the system family level. These can be modified to suit your company standards. Another useful graphic override is to create filters that display only the systems you want to see in a view. For example, use graphic override filters to display the sanitary piping only and not the hot and cold water piping, as shown in Figure A–10.

**Figure A–10**

## System Graphic Overrides

By default, in the Autodesk Revit templates, the Return Air Systems are magenta and Supply Air Systems are blue. In Figure A–11, Hydronic Supply and Return Systems also have the colors specified. System colors display in all views including 3D views.

**Figure A–11**

- System graphic overrides are consistent across the entire project. They are not view specific.

### How To: Set Up System Graphic Overrides

1. In the Project Browser, expand **Families>Piping** (or **Duct**) **Systems>Piping** (or **Duct**) **System**.

   *Note: To create a new system family, in the Project Browser, right-click on an existing type and duplicate it.*

2. Double-click on the one that you want to modify or right-click and select **Type Properties**.

3. In Type Properties, next to *Graphic Overrides*, click **Edit...**.

4. In the Line Graphics dialog box (shown in Figure A–12), make changes to the *Weight*, *Color*, and/or *Pattern.*

**Figure A–12**

5. Click **OK** twice to apply the changes.

# Using Graphic Override Filters

Any view can be set to display specific systems by using filters. In the example in Figure A–13, the view on the left displays all of the systems along with extra elements such as data components. The view on the right has graphic overrides that toggle off extraneous elements and filter out all systems except duct and hydronic piping.

**Figure A–13**

## How To: Apply a View Filter to Override a View

1.  Open the Visibility/Graphic Overrides dialog box.

2.  In the dialog box, select the *Filters* tab.

3.  In the *Visibility* column, select the overrides you want to display. In Figure A–14, the Domestic and Sanitary categories have been toggled off while the Mechanical systems display.

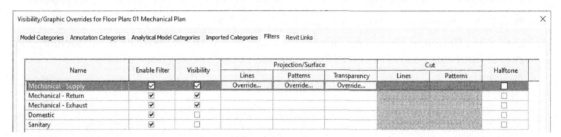

Figure A–14

4.  To add a new filter to this view, click **Add**.

5.  In the Add Filters dialog box (shown in Figure A–15), select the type of systems you want to modify and click **OK**.

    *Note: The list might vary depending on the filters set up in the project.*

Figure A–15

*   View filters override system graphics so any colors you set in this dialog box supersede those specified in the System Type.

- If you need to change information about the filter itself, click **Edit/New...** in the Add Filters or Filters dialog box. Then, modify the *Categories* or *Filter Rules*. For example, the **Mechanical - Exhaust Filter** does not include *Air Terminals* by default so you need to select it, as shown in Figure A–16.

**Figure A–16**

# A.6 Introduction to Revit Worksharing

When a project becomes too big for one person, it needs to be subdivided so that a team of people working on the same network can work on it. Since Revit projects include the entire building model in one file, the file needs to be separated into logical components, as shown in Figure A–17, without losing the connection to the whole. This process is called *worksharing* and the main components are worksets.

**Figure A–17**

Revit worksharing gives multiple team members connected on the same network the ability to co-author a single project model (one .RVT file). The appropriate team member creates a central model with multiple worksets (such as element interiors, building shell, and site) that are used by the project team members. Team members open and work in a local copy of the model that is linked back to the central model through saving and synchronizing. For more information about establishing and using worksets, refer to the ASCENT guide *Autodesk Revit: Collaboration Tools*.

A workshared project consists of one central model (also known as a central file) and individual models for each user known as local files, as shown in Figure A–18. Each team member will work in their local file and use a function called *synchronizing with central* to send and receive updates with the central model.

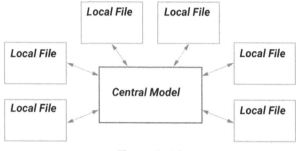

**Figure A–18**

- The **central model** is created by the BIM manager, project manager, or project lead and is stored on a server or in the cloud, enabling multiple users to access it.

- A **local file** is a copy of the central model that is stored on your computer.

- All local files are saved back to the central model, and updates to the central model are sent out to the local files. This way, all changes remain in one file, while the project, model, views, and sheets are automatically updated.

# Worksharing Definitions

**Worksharing:** This is a functionality that, when enabled, allows multiple members of the team to access a project stored in one centralized location, which gives multiple users the ability to work on the same project simultaneously.

**Workshared file:** This is a project that has worksets enabled. If the project has no worksets enabled, it is called a *non-workshared file*.

**Workset:** This is a collection of elements that are related geometrically, parametrically, or by location within an overall project that are subdivided so they can be worked on while isolated from the rest of the model. When worksharing is enabled, worksets are automatically activated and the *Workset1* and *Shared Grids and Levels* worksets are added to the project by default.

**Central model:** Also called the central file, this is the main project file that is stored on a local network that all users can access. Using a central model is called *file-based worksharing*. The central model stores workset and element information in the project and is the file to which everyone saves and synchronizes their changes. The central model updates all the local files with the latest model information. This file should not be edited directly.

**Local file:** This is a copy of the central model that is saved to your local computer. This is the file that you modify and work in. As you work, you save the file locally and synchronize it with the central model.

**Element borrowing:** This refers to the process of modifying items in the project that are not part of the workset you have checked out. This either happens automatically (if no one else has checked out a workset) or specifically, when you request to have control of the elements (if someone else has a workset checked out).

**Active workset:** The workset that displays in the Status Bar is the active workset. Any new elements that are added will be placed on this workset. As you work, you will change the active workset accordingly.

**Relinquish:** This releases or returns a checked-out workset so that others can work on the elements within that workset. If you do not release or relinquish your checked-out worksets, other users will get a warning that they cannot edit the workset until you relinquish it, and they are given the option to request to borrow the workset. **Relinquish All Mine** allows you to relinquish worksets without synchronizing to the central model.

**Reload Latest:** This updates your local file without you needing to synchronize with the central model.

## General Process of Using Worksets

1. Wait for the appropriate team member to enable worksharing, set up worksets, and create the central model.
2. Create a local file from the central model.
3. Work in your local file and select the worksets that you need to work on by verifying the active workset.

   - Work in your local model by adding, deleting, and modifying elements.
   - You may need to request to borrow elements in worksets that are currently checked out by other team members.

4. Save the local file as frequently as you would save any other project.
5. Synchronize the local file with the central model several times a day or as required by company policy or project status.

   - This reloads any changes from the central model to your local file and vice versa.
   - If the option to **Save Local File before and after synchronizing with central** is checked, your local file will be saved, but it is always recommended to save the local file yourself every time you synchronize to the central model.

## Opening Workset-Related Files

When you open a workset-related file, it creates a new local file on your computer. Do not work in the main central model.

# How To: Create a Local File

1. In the *File* tab or Quick Access Toolbar, click  (Open).

2. In the Open dialog box, navigate to the central model server location and select the central model. Do not work in this file. Select **Create New Local**, as shown in Figure A–19, and click **Open**.

| File name: | Modern-Hotel-Life.rvt | ⌄ |
|---|---|---|
| Files of type: | All Supported Files (*.rvt, *.rfa, *.adsk, *.rte) | ⌄ |

Worksharing

☐ Audit      ☐ Detach from Central      ☑ Create New Local      Open ▼      Cancel

Figure A–19

3. A copy of the project is created. It will have the same name as the central model with your Autodesk Revit username added to the end.

• If you are working with a recently used central model, it may display on the Home screen with the icon shown in Figure A–20. Clicking this file automatically creates a local copy of the model. The first time you use this option, a warning displays, as shown in Figure A–21.

Modern-Hotel

Figure A–20

**Create a new local**                                    ✕

By opening this central model, you will create a local copy of it.

To open the central model directly, click Open and navigate to the central model.

☐ Don't show this message again      OK      Cancel

Figure A–21

4. You can save the file using the default name, or use 🖫 (Save As) and name the file according to your office's standard. It should include *Local* in the name to indicate that it is saved on your local computer, or that you are the only one working with that version of the file.

• Delete any old local files to ensure that you are working on the latest version.

### How To: Work in a Workshared Project

1. Open your local file.

2. In the Status Bar, expand the *Active Workset* drop-down list and select a workset, as shown in Figure A–22. By setting the active workset, other people can work in the project but cannot edit elements that you add to the workset.

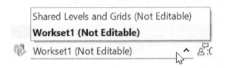

**Figure A–22**

3. Work on the project as needed.

## Saving a Workshared Project

When you are working on a workshared project, you need to save the project locally and centrally.

- Save the local file frequently (every 15-30 minutes). In the Quick Access Toolbar, click

  🖫 (Save) to save the local file just as you would any other project.

- Synchronize the local file with the central model periodically (every hour or two) or after you have made major changes to the project.

**💡 Hint: Set Up Notifications to Save and Synchronize**

You can set up reminders to save and synchronize files to the central model in the Options dialog box, on the *General* tab, as shown in Figure A–23.

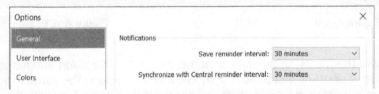

**Figure A–23**

# Synchronizing to the Central Model

There are two methods for synchronizing to the central model. In the Quick Access Toolbar or

*Collaborate* tab>Synchronize panel, expand  (Synchronize with Central) and click

 (Synchronize Now) or  (Synchronize and Modify Settings). The last-used command is active if you click the top-level icon.

- **Synchronize Now:** Updates the central model and then the local file with any changes to the central model since the last synchronization without prompting you for any settings. It automatically relinquishes elements borrowed from any workset but retains worksets used by the current user.

- **Synchronize and Modify Settings:** Opens the Synchronize with Central dialog box, shown in Figure A–24, so you can set the options for relinquishing worksets and elements, add comments, and specify to save the file locally before and after synchronization.

Figure A–24

- Always keep **Save Local File before and after synchronizing with central** checked to ensure your local copy is up to date with the latest changes from the central model.

- When you close a local file without saving to the central model, you are prompted to do so, as shown in Figure A–25.

**Figure A–25**

- The maximum number of backups for workset-enabled files is set to 20 by default.

- Note: Workshared files do not have the same backup files as non-workshared files.

# Command Summary

| Button | Command | Location |
|--------|---------|----------|
| **MEP Tools** | | |
| | **Building/Space and Type Settings** | • **Ribbon:** *Manage* tab>Settings panel, expand MEP Settings.<br>• **Ribbon:** *Analyze* tab> Reports and Schedules panel title |
| **Worksharing** | | |
| | **Save** | • **Quick Access Toolbar**<br>• *File* **tab:** Save<br>• **Shortcut:** <Ctrl>+<S> |
| | **Synchronize and Modify Settings** | • **Quick Access Toolbar**<br>• **Ribbon:** *Collaborate* tab>Synchronize panel, expand Synchronize with Central |
| | **Synchronize Now** | • **Quick Access Toolbar**<br>• **Ribbon:** *Collaborate* tab>Synchronize panel, expand Synchronize with Central |

# Additional Tools for Construction Documents

There are many other tools available in Revit® that you can use when creating construction documents. This appendix provides details about several tools and commands that are related to those covered in the Construction Documentation section of this guide.

## Learning Objectives

- Produce Pressure Loss reports.
- Use guide grids to help place views on sheets.
- Add revision clouds, tags, and information.
- Annotate dependent views with matchlines and view references.
- Import and export schedules.
- Place keynotes in a detail and add keynote legends that describe the full content of the keynotes

# B.1 Pressure Loss Reports

Pressure Loss reports are HTML files, as shown in Figure B–1, that include all of the data that can be viewed dynamically in the System Inspector. The reports can be set up to export exactly the information you need. They can be created for duct or pipe systems. The analysis for each system includes total pressure loss for the system and detailed information for various sections of duct or pipe.

| System Classification | Return Air |
|---|---|
| System Type | Return Air |
| System Name | 01 - RA01 |
| Abbreviation | |

**Total Pressure Loss Calculations by Sections**

| Section | Element | Flow | Size | Velocity | Velocity Pressure | Length | Loss Co |
|---|---|---|---|---|---|---|---|
| 1 | Duct | 500 CFM | 12"x12" | 500 FPM | - | 3' - 11 1/2" | - |
| | Fittings | 500 CFM | - | 500 FPM | 0.02 in-wg | - | 0.17 |
| | Air Terminal | 500 CFM | - | - | - | - | - |
| 2 | Duct | 1000 CFM | 12"x12" | 1000 FPM | - | 12' - 4 15/16" | - |
| | Fittings | 1000 CFM | - | 1000 FPM | 0.06 in-wg | - | 0.81490! |
| 3 | Fittings | 1000 CFM | - | 409 FPM | 0.01 in-wg | - | 0 |
| | Equipment | 1000 CFM | - | - | - | - | - |
| 4 | Duct | 500 CFM | 12"x12" | 500 FPM | - | 24' - 7 1/2" | - |
| | Fittings | 500 CFM | - | 500 FPM | 0.02 in-wg | - | 0.34 |
| | Air Terminal | 500 CFM | - | - | - | - | - |

Critical Path : 4-2-3 ; Total Pressure Loss : 0.14 in-wg

**Detail Information of Straight Segment by Sections**

| Section | Element ID | Flow | Size | Velocity | Velocity Pressure |
|---|---|---|---|---|---|
| 1 | 250437 | 500 CFM | 12"x12" | 500 FPM | 0.02 in-wg |
| | 250440 | 500 CFM | 12"x12" | 500 FPM | 0.02 in-wg |
| 2 | 250623 | 1000 CFM | 12"x12" | 1000 FPM | 0.06 in-wg |
| | 252421 | 1000 CFM | 12"x12" | 1000 FPM | 0.06 in-wg |
| | 252430 | 1000 CFM | 12"x12" | 1000 FPM | 0.06 in-wg |
| 4 | 250445 | 500 CFM | 12"x12" | 500 FPM | 0.02 in-wg |
| | 250446 | 500 CFM | 12"x12" | 500 FPM | 0.02 in-wg |
| | 250449 | 500 CFM | 12"x12" | 500 FPM | 0.02 in-wg |

**Figure B–1**

## How To: Create a Duct/Pipe Pressure Loss Report

1.  Select a system in a view. In the *Modify Duct (or Pipe) Systems* contextual tab>Duct (or Pipe) System Report panel, click  (Duct Pressure Loss Report) or (Pipe Pressure Loss Report). If you have not preselected a system in the view, in the *Analyze* tab>Reports & Schedules panel, select **Duct Pressure Loss Report** or **Pipe Pressure Loss Report**. The Pipe (or Duct) Pressure Loss Report - System Selector dialog box (shown in Figure B-2) enables you to select the systems that you want to include in the report.

Figure B-2

- To limit the systems displayed in the System Selector, click **System Type Filter** to open the dialog box shown in Figure B-3. Select the types of systems you want to include in the report and click **OK** to return to the main dialog box.

Figure B-3

- Use **Select All**, **Select None**, and **Invert Selection** to help with the selection.

2.  When you have finished selecting the systems to include, click **OK**.

3. In the Duct/Pipe Pressure Loss Reports Settings dialog box, specify the type of Report Format and the Reports Fields, and other information, as shown in Figure B–4.

**Figure B–4**

4. Click **Generate**.

# B.2 Working with Guide Grids on Sheets

You can use a guide grid to help you place views on a sheet, as shown in Figure B–5. Guide grids can be set up per sheet. You can also create different types with various grid spacings.

**Figure B–5**

- You can move guide grids and resize them using controls.

  **Note:** *When moving a view to a guide grid, only orthogonal datum elements (levels and grids) and reference planes snap to the guide grid.*

## How To: Add a Guide Grid

1. When a sheet is open, in the *View* tab>Sheet Composition panel, click ⊞ (Guide Grid).

2. In the Assign Guide Grid dialog box, select from existing guide grids (as shown in Figure B–6), or create a new one and give it a name.

**Figure B–6**

3. The guide grid displays using the specified sizing.

## How To: Modify Guide Grid Sizing

1. If you create a new guide grid you need to update it to the correct size in Properties. Select the edge of the guide grid.

2. In Properties, set the *Guide Spacing*, as shown in Figure B–7.

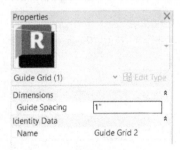

**Figure B–7**

# B.3 Revision Tracking

When a set of working drawings has been put into production, you need to show where changes are made. Typically, these are shown on sheets using revision clouds and tags along with a revision schedule in the title block, as shown in Figure B–8. The revision information is set up in the Sheet Issues/Revisions dialog box.

**Figure B–8**

- More than one revision cloud can be associated with a revision number.

- The title blocks that come with Revit already have a revision schedule inserted into the title area. It is recommended that you also add a revision schedule to your company title block.

- You have the ability to create multiple revision numbering sequences and you can use **Transfer Project Standards** to transfer these custom revision settings and revision numbering sequences to other projects.

- You can create a revision cloud schedule that can include multiple revisions. In a sheet view, from Properties, you can click **Edit...** and specify which revision you want to display on the sheet even if the revision is not on the sheet.

### How To: Add Revision Information to the Project

1. In the *View* tab>Sheet Composition panel, click 🗦 (Sheet Issues/Revisions).
2. In the Sheet Issues/Revisions dialog box, set the type of *Numbering* you want to use.
3. Click **Add** to add a new revision.
4. Specify the *Date* and *Description* for the revision, as shown in Figure B–9.

**Figure B–9**

- Do not modify the *Issued*, *Issued by*, or *Issued to* columns. You should wait to issue revisions until you are ready to print the sheets.

5. Click **OK** when you have finished adding revisions.

- To remove a revision, select its *Sequence* number and click **Delete**.

## Revision Options

- *Numbering:* Specify **Per Project** (the numbering sequence is used throughout the project) or **Per Sheet** (the number sequence is per sheet).

- *Row:* To reorganize the revisions, select a row and click **Move Up** and **Move Down**, or use **Merge Up** and **Merge Down** to combine the revisions into one.

- *Customize Numbering:* Click **Numbering...** to bring up the Numbering dialog box (shown in Figure B-10). You can edit the Alphanumeric or Numeric sequences or create custom sequences.

**Figure B-10**

- You can specify whether to create a new numbering sequence based off of **Numeric** or **Alphanumeric** as well as any prefix or suffix, as shown for the New Numbering Sequence dialog box in Figure B-11.

**Figure B-11**

- *Arc length:* Specify the length of the arcs that form the revision cloud. It is an annotation element and is scaled according to the view scale.

## How To: Add Revision Clouds and Tags

1. In the *Annotate* tab>Detail panel, click ☁ (Revision Cloud).
2. In the *Modify | Create Revision Cloud Sketch* tab>Draw panel, use the draw tools to create the cloud.
3. In Properties, select which *Revision* type to use, as shown in Figure B−12.

**Figure B−12**

4. Click ✔ (Finish Edit Mode).
- To modify a revision cloud, select a revision cloud, then in the Options Bar or Properties, expand the Revision drop-down list and select the revision, as shown in Figure B−13.

   *Note: If the revision table has not be set up, you can do this at a later date.*

**Figure B−13**

5. In the *Annotate* tab>Tag panel, click 🏷 (Tag By Category).
6. Select the revision cloud to tag. A tooltip containing the revision number and revision from the cloud properties displays when you hover the cursor over the revision cloud, as shown in Figure B−14.

**Figure B−14**

- If the revision cloud tag is not loaded, load **Revision Tag.rfa** from the *Annotations* folder in the Revit Library.

- The *Revision Number* and *Date* are automatically assigned according to the specifications in the revision table.

- Double-click on the edge of revision cloud to switch to Edit Sketch mode and modify the size or location of the revision cloud arcs.

- You can create an open cloud (e.g., as a tree line), as shown in Figure B−15.

**Figure B−15**

# Issuing Revisions

When you have completed the revisions and are ready to submit new documents to the field, you should first lock the revision for the record. This is called issuing the revision. An issued revision is noted in the tooltip of a revision cloud, as shown in Figure B−16.

**Figure B−16**

## How To: Issue Revisions

1.  In the *View* tab>Sheet Composition panel, click ⟲ (Sheet Issues/Revisions).

2.  In the Sheet Issues/Revisions dialog box, in the row for the revision that you are issuing, type a name in the *Issued to* and *Issued by* fields, as needed.

3.  In the same row, select **Issued**.

4.  Continue issuing any other revisions, as needed.

5.  Click **OK** to finish.

- Once **Issued** is selected, you cannot modify that revision in the Revisions dialog box or by moving the revision cloud(s). The tooltip on the cloud(s) note that it is **Issued**.

- You can unlock the revision by clearing the **Issued** option. Unlocking enables you to modify the revision after it has been locked.

# B.4 Annotating Dependent Views

The **Duplicate as a Dependent** command creates a copy of the view and links it to the selected view. Changes made to the original view are also made in the dependent view and vice-versa. Use dependent views when the building model is so large you need to split the building up on separate sheets, as shown in Figure B–17.

**Figure B–17**

- Using one overall view with several dependent views makes it easier to see changes, such as to the scale or detail level.

- Dependent views display in the Project Browser under the top-level view, as shown in Figure B–18.

**Figure B–18**

### How To: Duplicate Dependent Views

1. Select the view you want to use as the top-level view.
2. Right-click and select **Duplicate View>Duplicate as a Dependent**.
3. Rename the dependent views as needed.
4. Modify the crop region of the dependent view to show the specified portion of the model.

- If you want to separate a dependent view from the original view, right-click on the dependent view and select **Convert to independent view**.

## Annotating Views

To clarify and annotate dependent views, use **Matchlines** and **View References**, as shown in Figure B–19.

**Figure B–19**

- Sketch matchlines in the primary view to specify where dependent views separate. They display in all related views and extend through all levels of the project by default.
- View references are special tags that display the sheet location of the dependent views.

## How To: Add Matchlines

1.   In the *View* tab>Sheet Composition panel, click ▭ (Matchline).

2.   In the Draw panel, click ╱ (Line) and sketch the location of the matchline.

3.   In the Matchline panel, click ✔ (Finish Edit Mode) when you are finished.

*   To modify an existing matchline, select it and click ✔ (Edit Sketch) in the *Modify | Matchline* tab>Mode panel.

*   To modify the color and line type of Matchlines, in the *Manage* tab>Settings panel, click

     ▦ (Object Styles). In the Object Styles dialog box that opens, in the *Annotation Objects* tab, you can make changes to Matchline properties.

## How To: Add View References

1.   In the *View* tab>Sheet Composition panel or *Annotate* tab> Tag panel, click ⊞ (View Reference).

2.   In the *Modify | View Reference* tab>View Reference panel, search for or specify the *View Type* and *Target View*, as shown in Figure B−20.

**Figure B−20**

3.   Place the tag on the side of the matchline that corresponds to the target view.

4.   Click � key (Modify) to clear the selection.

5.   Repeat the process and place the tag on the other side of the matchline.

6. The tags display as empty dashes until the views are placed onto sheets. They then update to include the detail and sheet number, as shown in Figure B–21.

Figure B–21

- Double-click on the view reference to open the associated view.

- If only a label named **REF** displays when you place a view reference, it means you need to load and update the tag. The **View Reference.rfa** tag is located in the *Annotations* folder in the Revit Library. Once you have the tag loaded, in the Type Selector, select one of the view references and, in Properties, click 🔲 (Edit Type). Select **View Reference** in the drop-down list, as shown in Figure B–22, and click **OK** to close the dialog box. The new tag displays.

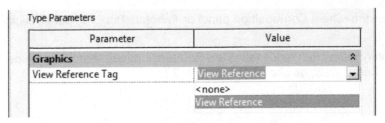

Figure B–22

# B.5 Importing and Exporting Schedules

Schedules are views and can be copied into your project from other projects. Only the formatting information is copied; the information about individually scheduled items is not included. That information is automatically added by the project the schedule is copied into. You can also export the schedule information to be used in spreadsheets.

## How To: Import Schedules

1.  In the *Insert* tab>Load from Library panel, expand ⬚ (Insert from File) and click ⬚ (Insert Views from File).

2.  In the Open dialog box, locate the project file containing the schedule you want to use.

3.  Select the schedules you want to import, as shown in Figure B–23.

    **Note:** *If the referenced project contains many types of views, change Views: to* **Show schedules and reports only***.*

**Figure B–23**

4.  Click **OK**.

## How To: Export Schedule Information

1. Switch to the schedule view that you want to export.

2. In the *File* tab, click 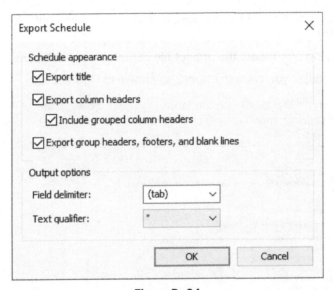 (Export)> (Reports)> (Schedule).

3. Select a location and name for the text file in the Export Schedule dialog box and click **Save**.

4. In the Export Schedule dialog box, set the options in the *Schedule appearance* and *Output options* areas that best suit your spreadsheet software, as shown in Figure B−24.

**Figure B−24**

5. Click **OK**. A new text file is created that you can open in a spreadsheet, as shown in Figure B−25.

| | A | B | C | D | E |
|---|---|---|---|---|---|
| 1 | Duct System Schedule | | | | |
| 2 | System Classification | System Name | Comments | Static Pressure | Flow |
| 3 | | | | | |
| 4 | Return Air | 01 - RA01 | RA | 0.11 in-wg | 1000 CFM |
| 5 | Return Air | 01 - RA02 | RA | 0.11 in-wg | 1000 CFM |
| 6 | Return Air | 01 - RA03 | RA | 0.11 in-wg | 1000 CFM |
| 7 | Return Air | 01 - RA04 | RA | 0.11 in-wg | 1000 CFM |
| 8 | Return Air | 01 - RA05 | RA | 0.11 in-wg | 1000 CFM |
| 9 | Return Air | 01 - RA06 | RA | 0.11 in-wg | 1000 CFM |
| 10 | Return Air | 01 - RA08 | RA | 0.11 in-wg | 1000 CFM |
| 11 | Return Air | 01 - RA09 | RA | 0.11 in-wg | 1000 CFM |
| 12 | Return Air | 01 - RA10 | RA | 0.11 in-wg | 1000 CFM |
| 13 | Return Air | 01 - RA11 | RA | 0.11 in-wg | 1000 CFM |
| 14 | Return Air | 01 - RA12 | RA | 0.09 in-wg | 500 CFM |
| 15 | Return Air | 01 - RA13 | | 0.11 in-wg | 500 CFM |

**Figure B−25**

# B.6 Keynoting and Keynote Legends

A keynote is a special kind of tag that applies specific numbers to various elements in a detail. Keynotes can be used on all model and detail elements, as well as materials. Using keynotes requires less room on a view than standard text notes, as shown in Figure B–26. The full explanation of the note is shown in a corresponding *keynote legend* placed elsewhere in the sheet or sheet set.

**Figure B–26**

- Keynote tags are found in the Revit Library in the *Annotations* folder and should be loaded into a project before you can apply them.

  *Note: By default, Revit uses the CSI master format system of keynote designations.*

There are three types of keynote tags:

- **Element:** Used to tag elements, such as a door, wall, or detail components.

- **Material:** Used for the material assigned to a component or applied onto a surface.

- **User:** A keynote that must first be developed in a keynote table.

## How To: Place a Keynote

1. In the *Annotate* tab>Tag panel, expand (Keynote) and click (Element Keynote), (Material Keynote), or (User Keynote).
2. Move the cursor over the element you want to keynote and select it.

3. If an element has keynote information assigned to it, the keynote is automatically applied. If it is not assigned, the Keynotes dialog box opens, as shown in Figure B–27.

Figure B–27

4. Select the keynote you need from the list of divisions and click **OK**.

- The options for keynotes are the same as for other tags, including orientation and leaders, as shown in Figure B–28.

*Note: The keynote remembers the leader settings from the last time it was used.*

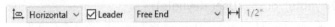

Figure B–28

### Hint: Setting the Keynote Numbering Method

Keynotes can be listed by the full keynote number or by sheet, as shown in Figure B–29. Only one method can be used at a time in a project, but you can change between the two methods at any time in the project.

1. In the *Annotate* tab>Tag panel, expand (Keynote) and click (Keynoting Settings).

Figure B–29

2. In the Keynoting Settings dialog box, specify the *Keynote Table* information and the *Numbering Method*, as shown in Figure B–30.

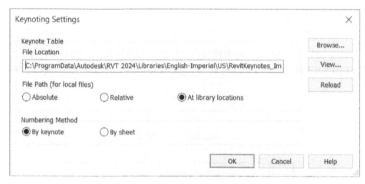

Figure B–30

- If you are using keynoting by sheet, create the Keynote Legend, and in the Keynote Legend Properties in the *Filter* tab, select **Filter by Sheet.**

- Keynotes are stored in a keynote table (a text file), as shown in Figure B–31. Any updates made to the keynote table are reflected in the project after it is closed and then re-opened.

RevitKeynotes_Imperial - Notepad

File   Edit   Format   View   Help

```
01000     Division 01 - General Requirements
02000     Division 02 - Sitework
03000     Division 03 - Concrete
04000     Division 04 - Masonry
05000     Division 05 - Metals
06000     Division 06 - Wood and Plastics
07000     Division 07 - Thermal and Moisture
08000     Division 08 - Doors and Windows
09000     Division 09 - Finishes
10000     Division 10 - Specialties
11000     Division 11 - Equipment
12000     Division 12 - Furnishings
13000     Division 13 - Special Construction
14000     Division 14 - Conveying
```

Figure B–31

# Keynote Legends

A keynote legend is a table containing the information stored in the keynote that is placed on a sheet, as shown in Figure B–32. In Revit, it is created in a similar way to schedules.

*Note: A keynote legend is different from a standard legend.*

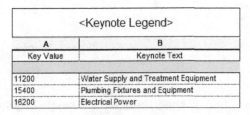

| <Keynote Legend> | |
|---|---|
| **A** | **B** |
| Key Value | Keynote Text |
| 11200 | Water Supply and Treatment Equipment |
| 15400 | Plumbing Fixtures and Equipment |
| 16200 | Electrical Power |

Figure B–32

## How To: Create a Keynote Legend

1. In the *View* tab>Create panel, expand ⊞ (Legends) and click ⊞ (Keynote Legend).
2. Type a name in the New Keynote Legend dialog box and click **OK**.

3. The Keynote Legend Properties dialog box typically only displays two scheduled fields, which are already set up for you, as shown in Figure B–33.

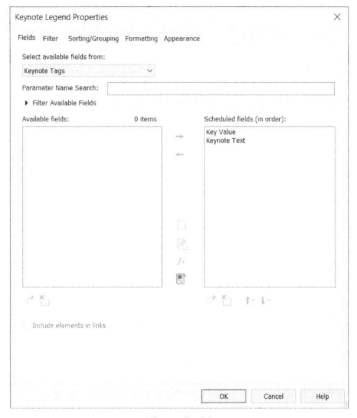

**Figure B–33**

4. In the other tabs, set up the format of the table as needed.

5. Click **OK** to create the keynote legend.

6. When you are ready to place a keynote legend, drag it from the Project Browser onto the sheet. You can manipulate it in the same way, similar to modifying other schedules.

• As you add keynotes to the project, they are added to the keynote legend.

# Command Summary

| Button | Command | Location |
|---|---|---|
| **Annotations** | | |
| | **Element Keynote** | • **Ribbon:** *Annotate* tab>Tag panel, expand Keynote |
| | **Material Keynote** | • **Ribbon:** *Annotate* tab>Tag panel, expand Keynote |
| | **User Keynote** | • **Ribbon:** *Annotate* tab>Tag panel, expand Keynote |
| | **Matchline** | • **Ribbon:** *View* tab>Sheet Composition panel |
| | **View Reference** | • **Ribbon:** *View* tab>Sheet Composition panel or *Annotate* tab>Tag panel |
| **MEP Tools** | | |
| | **Duct Pressure Loss Report** | • **Ribbon:** *Analyze* tab>Reports & Schedules panel |
| | **Pipe Pressure Loss Report** | • **Ribbon:** *Analyze* tab>Reports & Schedules panel |
| **Revisions** | | |
| | **Revision Cloud** | • **Ribbon:** *Annotate* tab>Detail panel |
| | **Sheet Issues/Revisions** | • **Ribbon:** *Manage* tab>Settings panel, expand Additional Settings |
| **Schedules** | | |
| | **Insert Views from File** | • **Ribbon:** *Insert* tab, expand Insert from File |
| n/a | **Schedule (Export)** | • ***File* tab:** expand Export>Reports>Schedule |
| | **Schedule/Quantities** | • **Ribbon:** *View* tab>Create panel, expand Schedules<br>• **Project Browser:** right-click on Schedule/Quantities node>New Schedule/Quantities... |

# Zones

Preparing a project so that you can run a systems analysis involves grouping spaces into zones that are heated and cooled in the same manner. Creating color schemes that graphically indicate the various zones is helpful. Using the System Browser, you can review existing zones and any spaces that have yet to be assigned to a zone.

## Learning Objectives

- Add zones to connect spaces for analysis.
- Use the System Browser with zones.
- Apply color schemes and color fill legends for spaces and zones.

# C.1 Creating Zones

After creating spaces, the next step in preparing to compute Systems analysis is to divide the building into zones, as shown in Figure C–1. Each zone consists of similar spaces that would be heated and cooled in the same manner.

**Figure C–1**

- There is always one **Default** zone in a project. All spaces are automatically attached to that zone when they are created.

- While you can add zones into a template, you usually add spaces first, then create zones and add spaces to the zones.

- You can create zones in plan and section views.

## How To: Add Zones

1.  Open a plan view that contains the spaces you want to work with. If you have a zone that spans across two levels, open a section view as well.

    *Note: You can set up a view template for zones in the same way as you set up one for spaces.*

2. For each view, open the Visibility/Graphic Overrides dialog box and on the *Model Categories* tab, in the *Visibility* column, check the checkbox next to **HVAC Zones**, then expand it and select all of the options, as shown in Figure C–2.

Figure C–2

3. Click **OK**.

4. In the *Analyze* tab>Spaces & Zones panel, click (Zone).

5. In Properties, under *Identity Data*, type a name for the Zone for the **Name** value. By default, the zones are numbered incrementally.

6. In the *Edit Zone* tab, ensure that (Add Space) is automatically selected.

7. Select the spaces that you want to add to the zone.

8. Click (Finish Editing Zone).

• Another quick way to add a zone is to select the spaces first, then in the *Analyze* tab>Spaces & Zones panel, click (Zone). The spaces are automatically added to the zone.

• To edit an existing zone, select one of the zone lines, as shown in Figure C–3, then in the *Modify | HVAC Zones* tab>Zone panel, click (Edit Zone). The *Edit Zone* tab displays, which enables you to add more spaces.

Figure C–3

• Click (Remove Space) to remove a space from the zone or modify the zone properties.

- Zones do not automatically have a tag placed, but it is helpful to display these as you are working. In the *Annotate* tab>Tag panel, click  (Tag by Category) and select on the zone(s) that you want to tag, as shown in Figure C–4.

**Figure C–4**

- You can change the name of a zone by changing the tag or in Properties. Zone tags are found in the Revit Library in the *Annotations>Mechanical* folder.

## Using the System Browser with Zones

The System Browser is a useful tool when working with systems, analytical systems, and zones. The System Browser is an effective tool that helps you in finding components that are or are not assigned to a system or zone. When you select a zone or space in the System Browser, it displays in the project, as shown in Figure C–5. The selected zone or space is automatically made active in the Properties. This enables you to modify names for spaces and zones and assign information, such as electrical loads and mechanical airflow.

**Figure C–5**

- You can open the System Browser using any of the following methods:

  - Press <F9>.

  - In the view, right-click, expand **Browsers**, and select **System Browser**.

  - In the *View* tab>Windows panel, expand (User Interface) and select **System Browser**, as shown in Figure C–6.

**Figure C–6**

- You can float or dock the System Browser to any side of the screen. You can also place it on a second monitor.

- The System Browser can be docked with Properties and the Project Browser to save screen space.

## How To: Use the System Browser with Zones

1. Open the System Browser by pressing <F9>.

2. If the zones are not displayed, expand the View drop-down list and select **Zones**, as shown in Figure C–7.

**Figure C–7**

3. All of the spaces are listed under the **Default** zone (as shown in Figure C−8) until they are added to a specific zone.

- Each space displays an icon showing its status: 🏠 (Occupiable), 🏠 (Not Occupiable),

  and 🏠 (Space not placed).
- As new zones are added, the spaces are moved into the new zones.

**Figure C−8**

4. Select a space or a zone. It is highlighted in the project and becomes active in the Properties.

- You can select more than one space or zone at a time using <Ctrl> and <Shift>.

- In the System Browser, if you right-click on a space or zone and select **Show**, you may get a message that says there are no open views that show any of the highlighted elements. Click **OK**. The software zooms in on the selected elements.

- If there is more than one view in which the space can be displayed, the Show Element(s) in View dialog box opens, as shown in Figure C−9.

**Figure C−9**

- If you place spaces and then delete them, they remain in the project. To delete a space entirely, in the System Browser, right-click on the space name and select **Delete**.

  - You can also delete spaces in a space schedule view.

# C.2 Applying Color Schemes

When working with zones and spaces, it is useful to have a view that displays color coding for individual zones, spaces, or rooms, as shown in Figure C–10. You can include a color fill legend in the same view to clarify the use of the colors.

**Figure C–10**

- Color schemes are controlled by a view property. Therefore, you should create a view for each color diagram that you want to include.

## How To: Set Up a Color Scheme in a View

1. Create or duplicate a view that you want to use for the color scheme.

2. In Properties, click the button next to the **Color Scheme** parameter, as shown in Figure C–11.

**Figure C–11**

3. In the Edit Color Scheme dialog box, in the *Schemes* area, select a **Category**.

4. Select a scheme in the list. In the example shown in Figure C–12, **Space Names** is selected.

**Figure C–12**

*Note: For information about creating color schemes, see A.3 Defining Color Schemes.*

5. Click **OK**. The new color scheme displays in the view.

- The color fill of the scheme can display in the background or foreground of the view. In Properties, set the *Color Scheme Location*. This impacts how components display and whether or not the color fill stops at the walls.

- You can add a legend that matches the Color Scheme, as shown in Figure C–13. In the *Analyze* tab>Color Fill panel, click ▤ (Color Fill Legend), and place the legend where you want it.

*Note: The Type Properties for the Color Fill Legend control the appearance of the legend, including the swatch size and text styles.*

**Figure C–13**

- If you change the **Color Scheme** in the View Properties dialog box, it also updates in the associated legend.

# Practice C1
# Create Zones

## Practice Objectives

- Add zones.
- Use the System Browser to identify and modify zone information.
- Create a color scheme showing the zones.

In this practice, you will add HVAC zones to the project. You will examine the zones and spaces in the System Browser and you set up a view that displays the zone names by color as shown in Figure C–14 with zone tags. Optionally, you can create additional zones.

Figure C–14

## Task 1: Add zones.

1. In the practice files *Working Models>General* folder, open **Gen-Zones.rvt**.
2. Duplicate the Coordination>MEP>Floor Plans>**01 Space Plan** view
3. Rename it **01 Zones Plan**.

4. Select one of the sections in the view and type **VH** to hide the category in the view.

5. Open the Visibility/Graphic Overrides dialog box, set the *Filter List* to **Mechanical**, and do the following in the *Visibility* column:

   • Select and expand the **HVAC Zones** node and check the checkboxes next to **Boundary**, **Interior Fill**, and **Reference Lines**.

   • Expand the **Spaces** node and clear the checkboxes for **Interior Fill** and **Color Fill**.

   *Note: You can still select the spaces, but the interior fill does not display.*

6. Click **OK**.

7. In the *Analyze* tab>Spaces & Zones panel, click ⬜ (Zone).

8. In the *Edit Zone* tab, verify that ⬜ (Add Space) is selected.

9. In the north wing, select the spaces across the top group of classrooms so the zone displays as shown in Figure C–15.

**Figure C–15**

10. In Properties, change the *Name* to **Classrooms 1**.

11. In the *Edit Zone* tab>Edit Zone panel, click ✔ (Finish Editing Zone).

12. Add another zone to the Classrooms and Storage Areas on the other side of the hall as shown in Figure C–16.

    *Note: The name of the zone automatically increments as each zone is added.*

Storage areas

**Figure C–16**

**13.** Add zones to the two classroom groups in the south wing.

**14.** Save the project.

## Task 2:  Use the System Browser.

**1.** Press <F9> to open the System Browser, if it is not already open.

**2.** In the System Browser, verify that the view displays **Zones**, as shown in Figure C–17.

**Figure C–17**

**3.** Expand the **Default** zone. Note that there are a lot of spaces that are not placed in zones. There are also two different types of icons for spaces: occupied (green icon) and unoccupied (orange icon), as shown in Figure C–18.

**Figure C–18**

**4.** Some of the spaces that should be unoccupied, such as the **200** and **201 Plumbing Chases** shown in Figure C–18, are not set correctly. In the System Browser, hold <Ctrl> and select the two plumbing chases.

**5.** In Properties, scroll down to the *Energy Analysis* area and clear **Occupiable**.

6. In the System Browser, in the default zone, right-click on one of the plenums and select **Show** (open additional views as necessary). If necessary, click **OK** or **Show** in the dialog box that displays to search for the zone in the project's views. The view changes to display the location of the plenum, such as the one shown in Figure C–19.

- Note: The view that is shown may differ from the one in the image depending on which plenum zone you selected in the System Browser.

**Figure C–19**

7. Close the Show Element(s) in View dialog box.

8. Click away from any elements to release the selection.

9. Close the System Browser.

10. Save the project.

## Task 3: Add a color scheme.

1. Ensure you are in the **01 Zones Plan** view. Zoom extents, if necessary, and close any extra view tabs.

   **Note:** In the Quick Access Toolbar, you can click 🗔 (Close Inactive Views).

2. In Properties, in the *Graphics* section, click the button next to *Color Scheme*.

3. In the Edit Color Scheme dialog box, in the *Schemes* area, change the *Category* to **HVAC Zones**.

**4.** Select the default **Schema 1**. The Scheme Definition automatically populates by zone name as shown in Figure C–20.

**Figure C–20**

**5.** In the *Schemes* area, rename *Schema 1* to **Zones**.

**6.** In the *Scheme Definition* area, in the *Title* field, type **Zones Legend**.

**7.** Click **OK**. The color scheme is applied to the view. The display will be similar to that shown in Figure C–21 (your zone colors may vary).

**Figure C–21**

• Open the Visibility/Graphic Overrides dialog box, expand **HVAC Zones**, and clear **Reference**.

*Note: Refer to A.3 Defining Color Schemes for more information on color schemes.*

8. In the *Analyze* tab>Color Fill panel, click  (Color Fill Legend) and place the legend near the classrooms, as shown in Figure C–22.

**Figure C–22**

9. Save the project.

## Task 4:  Add additional zones.

1. If time permits, add the zones listed below and shown in Figure C–23.
   - (1) The classroom zones (created in previous steps)
   - (2) All of the corridors plus the Electrical Room
   - (3) All of the vestibules
   - (4) Nurse's Office, Bookroom, Special Ed rooms, and Workroom
   - (5) Reception, Offices, and Copy Room
   - (6) Library and associated rooms
   - (7) Gym
   - (8) Cafeteria
   - (9) Kitchen and Kitchen Storage
   - (10) Restrooms
   - (11) Housekeeping, Janitor, and associated chases

**Figure C–23**

2. Save and close the project.

**End of practice**

# Chapter Review Questions

1. Zones (shown in Figure C–24) are formed of spaces that can be heated and cooled in the same manner.

**Figure C–24**

   a. True

   b. False

2. In the System Browser, in the Zones view,  displays next to the name of the space. What does it indicate?

   a. The space occupancy has not been defined.

   b. The space does not have an upper boundary.

   c. The space has not been placed.

   d. The space is not part of a zone.

**3.** You want to modify a view so that colors for the various zones display as shown in Figure C–25. How do you apply the colors to the view?

**Figure C–25**

a. Modify the color scheme in Visibility/Graphics.

b. Assign a color scheme in Properties.

c. Toggle on **Color Schemes** in the View Control Bar.

d. Add a Color Fill Legend.

# Command Summary

| Button | Command | Location |
| --- | --- | --- |
| | **Color Fill Legend** | • **Ribbon:** *Analyze* tab>Color Fill panel |
| | **Zone** | • **Ribbon:** *Analyze* tab>Spaces & Zones panel |

# Index

Made in the USA
Las Vegas, NV
25 February 2024

86292506R00157